exercises
for the
ocean yacht
navigator

exercises
for the
ocean yacht navigator

Kenneth Wilkes

Nautical

Copyright © H. Kenneth Wilkes MRIN 1976

First published in Great Britain 1976 by
NAUTICAL PUBLISHING CO LTD
Nautical House, Lymington, Hampshire SO4 9BA
in association with
George G. Harrap & Co Ltd,
182 High Holborn, London, WC1V 7AX

ISBN 0 245 52871 7

Filmset and printed by
BAS Printers Limited, Wallop, Hampshire

Contents

by the same author
Practical Yacht Navigator
Ocean Yacht Navigator

Introduction

There is nothing particularly difficult in working out sights of heavenly bodies taken with a sextant—called 'sight reductions'—except to get the answer right! The principles are simple, and the sight reduction tables now available eliminate any complex calculations.

Nevertheless, one has to look up a number of figures in almanac and tables, and to make a few simple additions and subtractions. Experience shows that while most people grasp the steps required, many make simple mistakes. This can only be overcome by practice, by meticulous attention to detail and by checking every figure before proceeding.

The purpose of this book is to provide practice in sight reduction work, and to give suggested layouts which will make the work as simple and straightforward as possible. I hope the book will be of value to students who have already studied the subject and require more practice, and also to experienced navigators who may have got a little 'rusty'. The problems may also be useful to instructors for setting students' exercises.

The book contains six chapters. Each chapter covers the whole range of sights of all navigational heavenly bodies. It starts with straightforward sun sights and progresses through stars, planets and the moon. Two questions cover Zone Time, Greenwich Date and the Date Line. Finally, for those interested, a great circle problem is given, and a few 'general sextant knowledge' questions.

Each chapter is arranged in the same sequence, later chapters containing problems which may involve a little more skill than the earlier ones. Problems are set in all parts of the world. The exercises may be worked through in alternative ways: either work through each chapter before proceeding to the next, or work the first question in each chapter. This will provide six questions on the same type of sight. Then work through question No 2 in each chapter, and so on.

All questions can be answered by reference to the Nautical Almanac

1975 (Nautical Almanac Office, Royal Greenwich Observatory and Nautical Almanac Office, U.S. Naval Observatory). For work at sea, of course, an almanac for the current year will be required. Extracts from the 1975 Almanac are in the back of the companion book to this, *Ocean Yacht Navigator*. Also there will be found extracts from Sight Reduction Tables for Air Navigation AP 3270 and HO 249 Vols. 1 & 3. These will enable all questions in Chapters 1, 2 & 3 to be worked. Chapters 4, 5 & 6 require all three volumes (Vols. 1, 2 & 3) of either AP 3270 or HO 249. These will of course be required for taking sights at sea. These tables last indefinitely and do not require replacing annually. For those who possess, or wish to use, NP 401, HO 229 or the older HD 486, many of the answers given show the results using any of these tables. As will be seen, the results may be fractionally different, but the differences are within the degree of accuracy that one can expect at sea.

For those who prefer to calculate their sight reductions, many answers show the full workings using the Marcq St Hilaire Haversine/Cosine formula method. These have been worked from the DR position. As this is different from a chosen position (used when working with sight reduction tables) the lengths of the intercepts will be different. However, when these are plotted the resulting position line will be found to correspond very closely with that obtained when using a chosen position.

All answers given show the full calculations and figures. If the student's answer is not within a mile of that given he could check off his workings with the calculations given, and trace where the difference lies. It will be noted that all the answers follow a pattern. Many navigators develop their own method of working and layout. Until one is able to get the correct answer with certainty, it is recommended that the sequence and layout given in the answers is followed. For this reason, and to make the work as realistic as possible, the answers are exactly as they might appear in a navigator's sight book.

Occasionally duplication of an item may be noticed (e.g. sun's declination; moon's HP). The reason for this is that it is much the best if *all* data from the almanac is written down in one operation. It can then be rearranged if necessary to make a subsequent operation easier. Thus, LHA, Lat., Dec., get grouped together to simplify finding the right figure in the tables. Note also that the captions CP Long. and CP Lat. are deliberately offset to the left, to facilitate picking these up when plotting on the chart.

The book *Ocean Yacht Navigator* gives a step-by-step explanation of the whole subject. Anyone with a basic knowledge of simple coastal navigation can fully master celestial navigation by working through it. *Ocean Yacht Navigator* gives, at the end of each chapter, a few simple exercises designed to ensure the reader has mastered the points in the chapter.

The present book takes the matter further by providing a series of practical problems, exactly as they may be encountered on a passage, together with fully worked solutions to enable the reader to verify his work, or, should he fail to get the correct answer, to see where he has gone wrong. In each of the first Answer section there is a footnote giving the chapter and page of *Ocean Yacht Navigator* which fully explains the subject.

Cover design by Peter Milne

Reproductions of charts and plotting sheets are with the sanction of H.M. Stationery Office and the Hydrographer of the Navy.

Arrangement of problems

* Extracts from Vol. 1 and 3, Sight Reduction Tables AP 3270, given in Ocean Yacht Navigator, will enable all questions in chapters 1 to 3 to be worked. For chapters 4 to 6, and for use at sea, Vols. 1, 2 and 3 Sight Reduction Tables AP 3270 or HO 249 will be required.

The extracts from Nautical Almanac 1975 given will enable all problems to be answered.

Geographical location of problems

Q.		Chapter					
		1.	2.	3.	4.	5.	6.
1.	Sun Mer. Pass.	48° N 14° W	38° N 73° W	15° N 59° W	39° S 155° E	47° N 134° W	30° S 50° E
2.	Sun sight	50° N 4° W	50° N 7° W	50° N 7° W	46° S 175° E	49° N 128° W	46° S 167° E
3.	Sun-run-Mer. Alt.	50° N 4° W	50° N 1° W	50° N 7° W	49° N 129° W	47° S 167° E	47° S 168° E
4.	Times of sunrise	52° N 3° E	36° N 12° W	49° N 123° W	35° S 172° E	8° N 70° E	42° N 65° W
5.	Zone Time	50° N 7° W	20° N 50° W	35° S 105° E	38° N 125° W	32° N 64° W	40° S 169° E
6.	Date Line ; GD	32° S 179° W	48° N 179° E	47° N 179° E	12° N 179° W	25° N 179° E	15° N 179° W
7.	Polaris	50° N 6° W	36° N 4° W	50° N 170° E	54° N 5° E	44° N 65° W	38° N 136° W
8.	Planet	50° N 3° W	50° N 6° W	50° S 92° W	20° S 87° E	47° N 134° W	42° S 163° E
9.	Stars, Vol. 1	50° N 6° W	50° N 6° W	50° N 174° E	39° S 167° E	32° N 25° W	42° S 157° E
10.	Stars, Vols. 2 & 3	50° N 3° W	50° N 6° W	50° S 92° W	50° S 92° W	32° S 152° E	34° S 152° E
11.	Moon sight	50° N 3° W	50° N 4° W	50° S 92° W	20° S 88° E	46° N 132° W	43° S 162° E
12.	Moon Mer. Pass.	57° N 10° W	43° S 43° E	52° N 40° W	44° S 54° W	51° N 127° W	40° S 158° E
13.	Multi. sight plot	50° N 6° W	50° N 171° E	50° N 6° W	20° S 87° E	34° S 152° E	34° S 152° E
14.	Compass check by sun Azimuth	50° N 4° W	50° N 128° W	50° N 70° W	47° S 167° E	10° N 165° E	39° S 143° E
15.	Series of sights	50° N 4° W	36° N 71° W	50° N 130° W	17° N 58° W	39° S 143° E	48° S 105° W
16.	Great circle	32° N 64° W / 51° N 10° W	33° S 72° W / 41° S 175° E	34° S 18° E / 35° S 56° W	34° S 18° E / 51° S 57° W	38° N 145° E / 48° N 128° W	30° S 32° E / 48° S 165° E

Abbreviations

ALRS	Admiralty List of Radio Stations
Alt.	Altitude
ATT	Admiralty Tide Tables
Az.	Azimuth
Cor.	Correction
CP	Chosen Position
CZD	Calculated Zenith Distance
Dec.	Declination
Dep.	Departure
D. Lat.	Difference in Latitude
D. Lon.	Distance in Longitude
DMP	Difference in Meridional Parts
DR	Dead Reckoning (position by)
DW	Deck Watch
DWE	Deck Watch Error
EP	Estimated Position
GD	Greenwich Date
GHA	Greenwich Hour Angle
GMT	Greenwich Mean Time
GP	Geographical Position
HMSO	Her Majesty's Stationery Office
HP	Horizontal Parallax
IE	Index Error (of sextant)
LHA	Local Hour Angle
Lat.	Latitude
Long.	Longitude
LL	Lower Limb (of sun or moon)
LMT	Local Mean Time
M	Mile(s)
m	Metre(s)
MP	Meridional Parts
Mer. Alt.	Meridian Altitude
Mer. Pass.	Meridian Passage
OP	Observed Position
PL	Position Line
PV	Prime Vertical
RDF	Radio Direction Finding
SHA	Siderial Hour Angle
TZD	True Zenith Distance
UL	Upper limb (sun or moon)
ZD	Zenith Distance
ZT	Zone Time

Chapter 1

1. On May 20th 1975 the yacht is in 48°20′ N 14°30′ W by DR. At what time by GMT should the sun be on the meridian ? If the sextant altitude of the sun's lower limb was then 61°30′·6 bearing S, what was the observed latitude ? Height of eye was 6 ft and index error 2′·0 on the arc.

2. On May 19th when in 49°50′ N 4°20′ W by DR a p.m. sun sight was taken when the time by chronometer (which was correct) was 15-54-33 GMT. The sextant altitude LL was 36°58′·8, the index error −2′·0 and ht of eye 6 ft. Give the chosen position and bearing and length of the intercept, ready for plotting on the chart.

3. On May 19th when in 49°50′ N 4°20′ W by DR an a.m. sun sight was taken at 07-53-15 GMT which gave the following results :
    CP 50° N 4°12′·4 W Intercept : AWAY 8·0, beating 096°.
   Yacht then sailed Co 240° T a distance by log of 21 M when a sun meridian altitude was taken.
    Give the GMT when the sun should be on the meridian of the fresh EP, and if the resulting latitude worked out to be 49°32′·5 N, what was the yacht's observed position then ?

4. What were the times (GMT) of dawn civil twilight and sunrise, and sunset and dusk civil twilight on August 29th in 52° N 3° E ?

5. The yacht has passed the Scilly Isles bound for Boston from England. When should the ship's clock be altered, and how should this be noted in the log book ? Would the chronometer or deck watch be altered ?

6. The yacht is on passage from Panama to New Zealand. On February 7th she is in about 32° S 179° W. The log book time column is headed Z + 12. You expect to cross the Date Line shortly. How would you handle the date in the log book, and the setting of the ship's clock and chronometer?

7. On May 19th when in 50° N 5°45' W by DR an observation of POLARIS is taken about dawn twilight when the time by chronometer is $3^h 55^m$. The sextant altitude was 49°49'·0. What was the yacht's latitude? Index error −4'·3 and ht of eye 8 ft.

8. On August 30th when in 50°20' N 2°50' W by DR a sight of JUPITER taken at 04-55-17 GMT gave a sextant altitude of 42°37'·7. IE was −4'·0 and ht of eye 8 ft. Give the CP and bearing and length of the intercept, ready for plotting the PL.

9. On May 21st when in 50°10' N 6° W by DR it is planned to take three star sights at dawn. Using AP 3270 Vol. 1 or HO 249 (Selected Stars), choose the three stars listed which are marked as being best placed in azimuth. List their names and their tabulated altitudes and bearings to assist identification.
If the sextant altitudes of these stars (in their listed order) were as follows, give the CP, and length and bearing of the intercept of each star:
1st star, at 03-53-44 GMT. Sextant Alt. 22°33'·8
2nd star, at 03-54-20 GMT. Sextant Alt. 48°17'·3
3rd star, at 03-55-05 GMT. Sextant Alt. 22°53'·2
Index error −4'·0, ht of eye 6 ft.

10. On August 31st when in DR 50°20' N 3°10' W the following stars were observed:
ALTAIR   at 19-53-12 GMT. Sextant Alt. 44°30'·0
ARCTURUS at 19-53-41 GMT. Sextant Alt. 33°16'·8
Index error was −1'·3 and ht of eye 8 ft.
Using Vol. 3 AP 3270 or HO 249 (see extracts in this book) find the

CP, the bearing and length of the intercept of each star, ready for plotting the OP.

11. On May 19th when in DR 50°20′ N 2°50′ W a sextant observation of the MOON's lower limb was 30°51′·7 at 16-53-22 GMT. The IE was −4′·0 and ht of eye 8 ft. Give the CP and length and bearing of the intercept ready for plotting the PL.

12. When in 56°50′ N 9°30′ W by DR on May 19th you propose finding the latitude by MOON's meridian altitude. At what GMT should the moon be on the meridian of the DR longitude?
If the sextant alt. of moon's UPPER limb were 33°05′·9 at meridian passage, what was the yacht's latitude then? Use IE −3′·3 and ht of eye 8 ft.

13. The yacht is in 50°15′ N 6°10′ W by DR when dawn twilight star sights are taken. The reductions are:
　　MIRFAK CP 50° N 5°36′·5 W Intercept TOWARDS 6·1, bearing 037°
　　ALTAIR　　　50° N 5°45′·5 W Intercept AWAY　　 18·0, bearing 170°
　　ARCTURUS 50° N 5°56′·8 W Intercept TOWARDS 2·5, bearing 273°
Plot the PLs on　**a)** Chart
　　　　　　　　b) Plotting Sheet
　　　　　　　　c) Squared paper
and state the OP.

14. On May 19th when in 49°50′ N 4°20′ W a check of the steering compass by sun's azimuth is taken at 07-53-15 GMT. The sun's bearing by the compass was 099° C. The variation locally was 7° W. What was the deviation on the yacht's heading at the time, and what was the total error of the compass?

15.a On May 19th when in 49°50′ N 4°20′ W by DR an a.m. sun sight was taken at 07-53-15 GMT, sextant alt. LL 30°37·3, Index error was −3′·0 and ht of eye 8 ft.

The yacht sailed Co 240° T a distance by log 21 M, when a sun meridian altitude was taken, sextant alt. LL 59°59'·5.
Same IE and ht of eye.
What was the OP then ?

b   As an accurate position was particularly desired, multiple sights were taken at dusk twilight the same evening (May 19th). Since the midday sight the yacht had sailed Co 292° T a distance of 48 M. The sights taken were

SATURN   at 20-52-10 GMT. Sextant Alt. 25°21·1
MOON LL   20-52-41 GMT. Sextant Alt. 37°23·2
ARCTURUS   20-53-05 GMT. Sextant Alt. 51°37·7
SPICA   20-53-50 GMT. Sextant Alt. 27°35·1
REGULUS   20-54-15 GMT. Sextant Alt. 43°52·7

Index error and ht of eye as before. AP 3270 Vol. 1 is not available—use Vol. 3. What was the OP ?

c   The next morning (May 20th) dawn twilight sights are taken. Since the previous evening sights, the log shows the yacht has sailed Co 264° T, distance 30 M. The observations were :

POLARIS   at 03-52-00 GMT. Sextant Alt. 49°33·4
Mirkaf   03-52-13 GMT. Sextant Alt. 21°10·4
ALTAIR   03-52-55 GMT. Sextant Alt. 48°37·1
ARCTURUS   03-53-25 GMT. Sextant Alt. 24°15·6

Index error −3'·0, ht of eye 8 ft.
What was the OP ?

16.   What is the length of a great circle track between points
near Bermuda 32° N 64° W
and Fastnet Rock 51° N 10° W
and how does this compare with a rhumbline between these two points ?

17.   When taking a sight, what do you understand by 'rocking the sextant', and why is this important ?

Chapter 2

1. On August 29th 1975 when in 38° N 73° W by DR a sun meridian altitude is required. At what time by chronometer should this be taken, and if the sextant altitude LL were 61°20'·2 bearing S, what was the latitude then? Index error −1'·3, ht of eye 8 ft.

2. On May 21st when in 49°45' N 6°50' W by DR the sun was observed at 09-54-52 GMT, sextant alt. LL 48°06'·0, IE −3'·0, ht of eye 5 ft. Give the Chosen Position and direction and length of the intercept ready for plotting.

3. On August 30th when in 50°10' N 1°40' W by DR, the sun was observed at 07-54-12 GMT. The sight reduction gave:
   CP 50° N 1°20·7 W. Intercept AWAY 8·3, bearing 105°
   At the sun's meridian passage a meridian altitude gave the latitude to be 50°14'·4 N. Between the morning and midday sights the yacht had sailed 24 M on Co 065° T and a tidal stream had been setting 255° at 1·5 kn. Find the OP at meridian passage.

4. What were the times (GMT) of dawn civil twilight and sunrise, and sunset and civil twilight on May 20th when in 36° N 12° W?

5. A yacht is sailing to U.K. from Bermuda and the ship's clock is set to Z + 4. When should the ship's clock and zone number in log book be altered, and which way?

6. The yacht is on passage from Japan to Vancouver and is approaching the Date Line in DR 48° N 179° E. The last entry in the log book time column is:

$$\begin{array}{c} Z - 12 \\ \text{June 14} \quad \overline{2300} \end{array}$$

What entry should be made as at midnight? How would ship's clock and/or chronometer be altered?

7. On August 31st when in 36° N 44° W POLARIS is observed at dusk when the time is 21-53-00 GMT. The sextant altitude is 35°56'·8, IE —3'·0, ht of eye 6 ft. What was the observed latitude?

8. On May 21st when in 50°05' N 6°10' W, VENUS is observed at 20-53-18 GMT. Sextant alt. 24°37'·5, IE 1'·4 OFF the arc, ht of eye 6 ft. Give the CP and direction and length of the intercept.

9. On August 31st when in 50°20' N 7° W it is proposed to take dusk sights of three stars, using AP 3270 Vol. 1 (Selected Stars) or HO 249. Find which stars are tabulated, select the three stars noted as being best placed in azimuth and list them, giving the tabulated alt. and bearing of each.

If these three stars were observed in the order in which they are tabulated, give the respective CP, Intercept and bearing of each. Use IE —1'·3, ht of eye 8 ft.

1st star at 19-52-28 GMT. Sextant Alt. 16°06'·3
2nd star at 19-53-12 GMT. Sextant Alt. 43°17'·1
3rd star at 19-53-41 GMT. Sextant Alt. 35°12'·0

10. Using AP 3270 or HO 249 Vol. 3 (assume Vol. 1, Selected Stars is not available), find the CP, Intercept and bearing of each of the following observations: DR 50°10' N 6°00' W on May 21st.

ALPHERATZ at 03-53-44 GMT. Sextant Alt. 33°41'·9
ALTAIR   03-54-20 GMT. Sextant Alt. 48°17'·3
ARCTURUS   03-55-05 GMT. Sextant Alt. 22°53'·2
Index error —4'·0, ht of eye 6 ft.

11. On May 19th when in 49°50′ N 4°20′ W by DR the MOON's lower limb was observed, sextant alt. 23° 13′·9 at 15-54-12 GMT. IE −2′·0, ht of eye 6 ft.
Give the CP, Intercept and bearing, ready for plotting.

12. When in 43° S 42°45′ E by DR on February 16th you were unable to take a sun mer. alt. and decide to take a MOON mer. alt. to establish the latitude of the yacht. If the DR's Long. is correct, at what time, GMT, will the moon be on your meridian?
If the MOON's LL sextant alt. were 33°25′·5 bearing N then, what is the latitude? IE −2′·2, ht of eye 6 ft.

13. When 50°20′ N 171°15′ E by DR, dawn sights gave the following results:
MIRFAK   Intercept TOWARD   8·8, bearing 026° CP 50° N 171°06·6 E
ALTAIR   Intercept AWAY   12·5, bearing 143° CP 50° N 170°56·8 E
ARCTURUS Intercept AWAY   8·2, bearing 257° CP 50° N 170°48·1 E
Plot the three PLs on chart, plotting sheet or on squared paper and give the resulting OP.

14. When the DR is 49°45′ N 128°40′ W on May 21st in the morning, the steering compass is checked by sun's azimuth at 16-55-14 GMT. The compass bearing of the sun was then 074° C. What was the total error of the compass on the yacht's heading at the time, and if the local variation was 24° E, what was the deviation?

15.a The yacht is on passage from Norfolk Va (U.S.A.) to Bermuda. On August 29th when in 36°10′ N 71°20′ W by DR the following dawn sights are taken at about 05ʰʳˢ Z + 5 time. Use Vol. 2, AP 3270 or HO 249; find the OP:
POLARIS at 09-52-13 GMT. Sextant Alt. 36°45′·0
RIGEL   at 09-52-48 GMT. Sextant Alt. 40°29′·5

SIRIUS   at 09-53-10 GMT. Sextant Alt. 21°30'·0
JUPITER at 09-53-57 GMT. Sextant Alt. 50°09'·0
IE −1'·6, ht of eye 8 ft.

b   The yacht then sailed for approx. 2 hours Co 115° T a distance by log
12·5 M. Current was estimated to be setting 040° at 2 kn. An a.m.
sight of SUN was taken :
SUN 11-52-09 GMT. Sextant Alt. LL 19°16'·0
IE and ht of eye as before.

c   A meridian altitude of the sun was taken after the yacht had sailed
Co 125° T for 27 M. Current now estimated at 1 kn setting 040°. The
sextant altitude was 63°33'·7 LL. IE and ht of eye unchanged. Find
the OP.

d   This PL was crossed with a MOON sight taken a few minutes later, at
16-52-21 GMT, Sextant alt. LL 3°17'·1, IE and ht of eye the same. Plot
and determine the OP.

e   After sailing Co 125° T for 28 M, current now estimated setting 040° at
1 kn, the sun was observed LL 26°41'·8 at 20-53-18 GMT, IE and ht
of eye as before.

f   At dawn the next day, August 30th, the yacht has sailed 29·5 M by log,
Co 150° T and current is estimated at 090° 1 kn. The three stars
tabulated as being best placed in azimuth were observed at the
following times and in the order listed in Vol. 1, Selected Stars :
1st star at 09-52-07 GMT. Sextant Alt. 22°42'·2
2nd star at 09-52-49 GMT. Sextant Alt. 42°24'·2
3rd star at 09-53-18 GMT. Sextant Alt. 43°13'·8
IE and ht of eye as before.
Find the OP.

16.   Plans are being made for a passage from Valparaiso to Wellington N.Z.
From position 33° S 72° W to 41° S 175° E, what is the distance along
a great circle track, and how does this compare with a rhumbline
distance ?

17. What checks would you apply to your sextant periodically to ensure that the mirrors are correctly set ? If any adjustments are found necessary, in what sequence should they be carried out ?

Chapter 3

1. A sight for a meridian altitude is to be taken on May 19th 1975, when in 15°10′ N 59°15′ W by DR. At what time (GMT) will the sun be on the meridian of the DR?

If the sextant alt. LL was then 84°59′·7 bearing N, what would be the observed latitude? Use IE 2′·0 OFF the arc, and ht of eye 8 ft.

2. On February 17th when in 50°15′ N 6°50′ W by DR the sun is observed at 09-52-05 GMT, sextant alt. LL 17°27′·0. Index error −1′·9, ht of eye 8 ft. What is the CP and intercept length and bearing?

3. On February 17th when in 50°15′ N 6°50′ W by DR a morning sun sight gave the following results:

CP 50° N 6°29′·9 W. Intercept AWAY 13·4, bearing 137°

The yacht then sailed a distance by log 13·8 M, Co 215° T when a sun mer. alt. gave the latitude as 49°57′ N. What was the yacht's OP then?

4. What is the time (GMT) of Moonrise on August 30th 1975 when in 32° N 54° W?

5. The yacht is on passage from Perth, Australia to Durban, S.A., and is in 35° S 105° E by DR. The log book has been correctly entered with Z − 7 at the head of time column, and the ship's clock corresponds. On February 16th a dawn star sight is taken when the ship's clock reads 5ʰ 05ᵐ. The chronometer, which is 2ᵐ 18ˢ slow, shows 10ʰ 07ᵐ 34ˢ. What is the GD and time GMT to use for the sight?

6.a Sailing eastward when in 47° N 179°30′ E by DR an evening star sight is taken when the chronometer (which has no error) shows 8ʰ 21ᵐ 15ˢ. The (local) date, shown in the log book, is June 10th and the book is headed Z — 12. What is the GD and GMT to use for the sight?

b The Date Line is taken as having been crossed during the night. The next morning a twilight star sight is taken when the chronometer (still correct) shows 3ʰ 8ᵐ 45ˢ. What is the GD and GMT to use for this sight? Show how this is arrived at.

7. The yacht's DR position is 50° N 170° E. At morning twilight on May 21st when the (correct) chronometer shows 3ʰ 54ᵐ 45ˢ POLARIS is observed, sextant alt. 49°40′·2. Index error is —4′·2 and ht of eye is 6 ft. What is the yacht's latitude?

8. On February 16th when in DR 50°15′ S 92° W an evening sight of SATURN is taken when the chronometer, which has no error, shows 01-55-33 GMT. Sextant alt. is 15°12′·7. Index error is 3′·0 OFF the arc and ht of eye is 6 ft. Give the CP and intercept length and bearing you would use to plot the PL.

9.a When in DR 50°20′ N 173°45′ E on May 20th it is planned to take dawn twilight star sights. Using Vol. 1 AP 3270 or HO 249 (Selected Stars), list the three stars which are marked in the tables as being those best placed in azimuth, and give their tabulated alts. and bearings to assist identification.

b If the observations of these three stars (in the order as tabulated) were as follows, give the respective CP, intercept and bearing of each star, ready for plotting:
    1st star at 15-52-56 GMT. Sextant Alt. 21°47′·8
    2nd star at 15-53-35 GMT. Sextant Alt. 48°08′·0
    3rd star at 15-54-10 GMT. Sextant Alt. 24°02′·5
Index error, —3′·4, ht of eye 10 ft.

10. When in DR 50°15' S 92° W, an evening star sight is taken on February 16th (local date). Using Vol. 3 AP 3270 or HO 249 (assume Vol. 1 selected stars is not available), find the CP, intercept length and bearing:
BETELGEUSE at 01-52-47 GMT. Sextant Alt. 32°19'·8
Index error off the arc 3'·0, ht of eye 6 ft.

11. On February 16th when in 50°15' S 92° W by DR the MOON is observed in the evening. Chronometer time 01-52-12 GMT, sextant alt. LL 8°53'·0. Index error, +3'·0, ht of eye 6 ft. Give the CP and intercept and bearing ready for plotting.

12.a When in DR 52°20' N 40° W on May 20th, no midday sun sight for latitude was possible due to cloud. It is therefore proposed to take a MOON Mer. Alt. At what GMT will the moon be on the meridian of the DR longitude?

b The MOON's Mer. Alt. was observed then, sextant altitude LL 31°13'·7 bearing S. Index error was −3'·2 and height of eye 8 ft. What was the latitude of the position then?

13. On August 31st the DR position was 50°20' N 6°10' W. Star sights were taken which gave the following results:
MIRFAK   CP 50° N 6°29'·1 W Intercept TO   24·0, bearing 026°
ALTAIR   50° N 6°40'·1 W Intercept AWAY 7·9, bearing 143°
ARCTURUS   50° N 6°47'·4 W Intercept AWAY 22·4, bearing 257°
Plot the OP and state lat. and long.

14. When in 49°50' N 70°40' W on August 29th the steering compass is checked for error. For this purpose the sun is observed at 11-52-09 GMT when the bearing of the sun by steering compass was 111° C. What was the total error of the compass, and if the variation there was 21° W, what was the deviation on the yacht's heading at the time?

15.   A yacht is on passage to Vancouver.

  a   On May 19th when in DR 50°10′ N 129°30′ W, dawn sights are taken as follows:

      POLARIS   at 11-53-05 GMT. Sextant Alt. 50°05′·0

      ARCTURUS   11-53-51 GMT. Sextant Alt. 26°28′·9

  Index error −1′·9, ht of eye 6 ft. Plot and state the OP.

  b   Yacht then sails Co 115° T, distance by log 68 M, when simultaneous sights of the SUN and MOON are taken in the afternoon of the same day:

      SUN   at 00-55-09 GMT. Sextant Alt. LL 29°46′·2

      MOON   00-55-47 GMT. Sextant Alt. LL 25°26′·5

  Index error and ht of eye as before. Plot the OP.

  c   During the night May 19th/20th the wind is very light. Co steered was 110° T and the log showed 17·5 M sailed since the afternoon sight on 19th. Dawn twilight star sights are taken on 20th:

      MIRFAK   at 11-53-40 GMT. Sextant Alt. 21°03′·9

      ALTAIR   11-54-10 GMT. Sextant Alt. 48°41′·5

      ARCTURUS 11-54-45 GMT. Sextant Alt. 24°15′·6

  Index error −1′·9, ht of eye 6 ft. Plot and state the OP.

16.   What is the distance along a great circle track from off Capetown, 34° S 18° E to off Montevideo 35° S 56° W, and how much shorter is this than a rhumbline between these two points? Determine intermediate points along the great circle track at intervals of 10° of longitude, using Great Circle Diagram No. 5029, or any other means.

17.   Radio reception is difficult, and only occasionally is a radio time check possible. The following are obtained:

      May   4th chronometer error 2ᵐ 44ˢ Fast

      May 11th chronometer error 2ᵐ 54ˢ Fast.

  Then the radio goes unserviceable. A sight is taken on June 17th when the time by chronometer is 08ʰ 14ᵐ 45ˢ. What is the GMT to use for the sight?

Chapter 4

1.a On February 16th 1975 when in 39° S 154°45′ E by DR a sun meridian altitude is required. At what GMT should this be taken if the DR is correct?

b. The sextant alt. sun's LL is then found to be 63°43′·1 bearing N. Index error is — 3′·0 and ht of eye 5 ft. What is the yacht's latitude?

2. On February 17th when in 45°50′ S 174°45′ E by DR an afternoon sun sight is taken. The chronometer, which has no error, shows 4ʰ 52ᵐ 18ˢ and the sextant alt. LL is 26°20′·4. Index error is —2′·5 and ht of eye 8 ft. Give the chosen position and the length and direction of the intercept, ready for plotting.

3. On May 21st when in 48°45′ N 128°40′ W by DR a forenoon sun sight is taken at GD 21ᵈ 16-55-14 GMT. This gave
 CP 49° N 128°40′·7 W, Intercept TO 12·6, Bearing 104°
The same day a sun meridian alt. is taken after the yacht has sailed a distance by log 28·4 M on Co 100° T. This gave the latitude as being 48°33′ N.
What was the OP at Mer. Pass.?

4. What were the GMTs of Civil twilight and sunrise, and of sunset and civil twilight on August 30th when in DR 35° S 172° E?

5. The yacht is bound for Honolulu from San Francisco and is in 38° N 125° W by DR. About evening twilight on May 20th (local date) a star sight is taken. The chronometer, which is $2^m 34^s$ fast, shows $4^h 1^m 48^s$ when the sight is taken. What is the Greenwich Date and GMT to use for the sight reduction?

6.   A yacht is sailing westwards; the position is about 12° N 179°30' W. The last entry in the log book reads:

$$\frac{Z + 12}{July 4. \quad 2345}$$ She expects to cross the date line during the night.

What alterations to clocks, and what entries in the log book would you make?

7.   On February 15th when in 54° N 5°20' E by DR a dawn sight of POLARIS is taken. Time, 06-55-45 GMT, sextant alt. 53°25'·0. Index error − 4'·0, ht of eye 6 ft. What was the observed latitude?

8.   On August 31st when in 20° S 87° E a dawn sight of MARS gives sextant alt. 48°55'·7 when the chronometer (which is correct) shows $11^h 52^m 9^s$. IE is − 0'·8, ht of eye 6 ft. Give the CP, intercept and bearing, ready for plotting.

9.a   The yacht is in 38°50' S 167° E by DR on February 17th. You propose taking star sights at dawn twilight. Using the time of dawn civil twilight as a guide, and Vol. 1 AP 3270 or HO 249, Selected Stars, state the three stars listed as being best placed in azimuth, and give the altitude and bearing of each.

   b   The three stars so selected are observed in the sequence in which they are listed, as follows:
         1st star at 17-52-24 GMT. Sextant Alt. 65°29'·7
         2nd star at 17-53-02 GMT. Sextant Alt. 58°00'·0
         3rd star at 17-53-41 GMT. Sextant Alt. 56°32'·2
      IE − 3'·0, ht of eye 6 ft.
      Plot and state the OP.

10. Assume Vol. 1 Selected Stars is not available and use Vol. 3 for this question.
On February 16th when in DR 50°15′ S 92° W an evening observation of ALDEBARAN is taken when the chronometer (which is correct) shows 1 h 53 m 49 s. Sextant alt. is 22°21′·0, IE 3′·0 off the arc, ht of eye 6 ft.
Give the CP, intercept and bearing, ready for plotting.

11. In the evening of May 21st when in DR 20°20′ S 88° E an observation of the MOON was made when the chronometer, which was correct, showed 10 h 53 m 34 s. The moon's sextant alt. was LL 31°57′·4. IE 2′·3 on the arc, ht of eye 8 ft.
Find the CP, intercept and bearing, ready for plotting.

12.a On August 29th when in DR 44° S 54° W it is proposed to observe the MOON's mer. alt. to obtain the latitude. If the DR is about correct for long., at what GMT will the moon be at meridian passage, to the nearest minute?

b And if the sextant alt. LL was 25°38′·9 at mer. pass., what was the latitude? IE −1′·0, ht of eye 6 ft.

13. When in DR 20° S 87° E star observations gave the following results:

SIRIUS	CP 20° S 86°56′·1 E. Intercept, AWAY 2·6	Zn 091°
ACHERNAR	20° S 86°47′·1 E. Intercept, TO 3·0	208°
HAMAL	20° S 86°36′·8 E. Intercept, AWAY 13·0	322°

What was the observed position?

14. When in 46°41′ S 167°20′ E by DR in the afternoon of February 15th at 05-53-50 GMT, a compass check is made by sun's azimuth. The bearing of the sun by steering compass was 271° C, and variation locally was 12° E. What was the total error of the compass on the yacht's heading at the time, and what was the deviation?

15.a On passage from Antigua, when in 17°10′ N 58°15′ W by DR on February 16th, dawn star sights are proposed. Using Vol. 1 AP 3270 or HO 249 (Selected Stars), find the three stars which will be best placed in azimuth. List their approximate altitudes and bearings, ready for taking the sights.

About dawn that day, the three selected stars (in the order listed in the tables) gave the following results:

    1st star at 09-52-15 GMT. Sextant Alt. 29°52′·5
    2nd star at 09-52-48 GMT. Sextant Alt. 45°22′·7
    3rd star at 09-53-10 GMT. Sextant Alt. 50°06′·0

Index error was − 4′·0, ht of eye 8 ft. What was the OP?

b A forenoon sun sight is taken at 11-54-37 GMT the same day, when the yacht has sailed Co 075° a distance by log 18 M since the dawn sights. The sun's sextant alt. was LL 21°25′·7. Give the CP, intercept and bearing, and plot the PL. IE and ht of eye as for last sights.

c The yacht maintains Co 075° T for 19 M when a sun mer. alt. is taken. At what time GMT will this occur, and if the sun's sextant alt. LL was 60°00′·6 bearing S, what was the OP then? IE and ht of eye as before.

d At evening twilight the same day when the yacht had run 34 M on Co 080° T since midday, the following were observed:

    MOON at 21-54-11 GMT. Sextant Alt. LL 58°57′·9
    VENUS   21-54-58 GMT. Sextant Alt. LL 22°08′·2
    RIGEL   21-55-32 GMT. Sextant Alt. LL 57°49′·3

IE and ht of eye as before. What was the OP?

16. A passage from Capetown to the Falkland Isles is being planned. Compare the distance along a great circle track with that of a rhumbline between points 34° S 18° E and 51° S 57° W.

17. From the following series of sights of the sun, determine the best figure to use for a sight reduction calculation:

    09-09-55 GMT. Alt. 42°51′·6
    09-10-50 GMT. Alt. 42°58′·1   09-12-32 GMT. Alt. 43°13′·0
    09-11-10 GMT. Alt. 43°09′·7   09-13-09 GMT. Alt. 43°17′·8

Chapter 5

1.a A sun meridian altitude sight is required on August 31st 1975 when the position by DR is 47°20′ N 133°45′ W. If the DR long. is about correct, at what time by ship's clock should this be taken if the zone time being kept is Z + 9, and what would the chronometer show, assuming it has no error?

  b If the sun is observed at that time, sextant alt. LL 50°59′·2, what was the observed latitude? Take index error as − 2′·0 and ht of eye 8 ft.

2. A forenoon sun sight is taken on May 21st when in 48°45′ N 128°40′ W by DR. The chronometer, which is correct, shows 4ʰ 55ᵐ 14ˢ. Index error is − 2′·8 and ht of eye 8 ft. The sextant alt. sun's LL is 38°31′·3. Find the CP and intercept and bearing ready for plotting.

3.a On February 15th (local date) when in 47°10′ S 166°55′ E by DR a sun merid. alt. is required. The ship's clock is set to Z −11 and is correct. At what time by ship's clock (to the nearest minute) should the sun be on the meridian of the DR, and what would be the GMT shown by the chronometer, assuming it had no error?

  b The latitude was then found to be 47°01′·8 S by sun's mer. alt.:

  c The yacht sails Co 040° T a distance by log 26·4 M when an afternoon sight is taken, giving a CP 47° S 167°05′·7 E, intercept AWAY 11·5, bearing 275°. What was the OP then?

4. What are the times (GMT) of Moonrise and Moonset on the night May 20th/21st when in 22° S 88° E?

5. On passage to Hamilton, Bermuda, a morning sun sight is taken on August 29th. The DR position is 32°30′ N 64° W. The ship's clock is not working. The chronometer, which is 7^m 34^s slow, shows 1^h 9^m 45^s. What is the GD and GMT to use for the sight?

6. The yacht is sailing from Japan to Honolulu and is in DR 25° N 179°30′ E. The last log book entry reads:

   $$\frac{Z - 12}{\text{July 3rd} \quad 2230}$$

   It is reckoned she will cross the date line during the night. How would the first log book entry after midnight appear, and how would ship's clock and chronometer be dealt with?

7. The yacht's DR position is 44° N 65°30′ W when a dawn sight of POLARIS is taken on May 19th at 07-52-15 GMT. Sextant alt. is 44°09′·1, index error −1′·5, ht of eye 8 ft. What is the observed latitude?

8. On May 20th (local date) when in 47° N 134° W an evening sight of VENUS is taken when the chronometer (which is correct) shows 4^h 54^m 37^s. The sextant alt. is 29°13′·7. Index error − 2′·0, ht of eye 8 ft.
   Find the CP, intercept and bearing, ready for plotting.

9.a It is planned to take star sights at evening twilight (use civil twilight) on February 17th when in DR 32°15′ N 25°15′ W. Using Vol. 1, Selected Stars, list the four stars shown as being the *brightest* stars then, and give their respective approximate altitudes and bearings to assist identification.

   b Observations of these four stars (given in the sequence in which they are tabulated) were as follows:
   1st star observed at 19-53-25 GMT. Sextant Alt. 41°57′·2
   2nd star observed at 19-54-10 GMT. Sextant Alt. 32°41′·8
   3rd star observed at 19-54-50 GMT. Sextant Alt. 27°33′·3
   4th star observed at 19-55-15 GMT. Sextant Alt. 46°10′·1
   Index error was −0′·8 and ht of eye 6 ft.
   Find the observed position.

10. At evening twilight on August 29th (local date) when in 34°10′ S 152° E by DR, ALTAIR was observed at 07-53-12 GMT. Sextant alt. was 26°10′·4, IE −4′·2, ht of eye 8 ft. Using Vol. 2 AP 3270 or HO 249 (assume Vol. 1 not available) find the CP, intercept and bearing ready for plotting.

11. When in 46°15′ N 132°30′ W by DR the MOON is observed in the afternoon of May 19th at about 4 p.m. by ship's clock (set to Z + 9). The chronometer, which was correct, showed 12ʰ 53ᵐ 37ˢ. The sextant alt. of moon's upper limb was 24°55′·4, index error −2′·0, ht of eye 10 ft. Give the CP, intercept and bearing, ready for plotting.

12.a On May 20th when in 51° N 127° W by DR, bound for Vancouver, it is planned to take a mer. alt. of the MOON in the evening to provide the latitude. Find the time, GMT, when the moon will be on the meridian of the DR.

   b If the sextant alt. of moon's lower limb at mer. pass. was 31°40′·9, what was the latitude then ? IE −1′·7, ht of eye 8 ft.

13. On August 29th when in DR 34°10′ S 152° E the following stars were observed, with results as shown :
    ALTAIR   CP 34° S 152°12′·1 E Intercept AWAY 8·5, bearing 058°
    SPICA   34° S 152°35′·8 E Intercept TO   17·9, bearing 287°
    ARCTURUS   34° S 152°06′·0 E Intercept AWAY 12·0, bearing 323°
    Plot the observed position.

14. The yacht is in 10°20′ N 65°30′ E on May 21st when the steering compass is checked for error. At 11-53-56 GMT the sun's bearing by compass is 287° C. What is the total error on the yacht's heading at the time, and if variation locally is 3° W, what is the deviation ?

15.a On February 16th when in DR 39°20′ S 143°30′ E a forenoon sun sight was taken when the ship's clock (set to Z − 10) showed 7·55 a.m. The chronometer (which was correct) showed $9^h 54^m 13^s$ when a sextant alt. was LL 22°09′·2. IE − 3′·0, ht of eye 10 ft.

A sun mer. alt. was observed when the yacht had sailed Co 080° T, distance 22 M since the morning sight, sextant alt. LL 63°08′·5, bearing N. Find the OP.

b Dusk star sights are proposed for that evening. Work up a new DR for the expected position at end of civil twilight, Co now 085° T. Using Selected Star Tables, list the three stars marked as being best placed in azimuth, with their approximate altitudes and bearings, for identification.

These three stars were observed, in the sequence in which they are tabulated, as follows, the yacht having sailed Co 085° T a distance 38 M since the midday OP:
   1st star at 09-53-33 GMT. Sextant Alt. 60°31′·7
   2nd star at 09-54-05 GMT. Sextant Alt. 27°31′·3
   3rd star at 09-54-37 GMT. Sextant Alt. 27°44′·3
IE − 3′·0, ht of eye 10 ft. Determine the OP.

c At dawn the next morning (local date Feb. 17th) when the yacht had sailed 44 M by log on Co 068° T since the previous evening's observations, the following sights were taken:
   MARS   at 18-53-49 GMT. Sextant Alt. 25°06′·2
   ACRUX   18-54-08 GMT. Sextant Alt. 60°22′·9
   SPICA   18-54-47 GMT. Sextant Alt. 59°22′·1
IE still − 3′·0 and ht of eye 10 ft. Find the OP.

16. A voyage is being planned from Tokyo to Seattle. Check the difference in mileage between a great circle track and a rhumbline between 38° N 145° E and 48° N 128° W.

17. How often, and at what time should an 8-day chronometer be wound up?

Chapter 6

1. On February 15th 1975 when in 30°20' S 50°30' E by DR the latitude
    by sun's mer. alt. is required.
    At what time, GMT, will the sun be on the meridian of the DR?
    If the sextant alt. LL is 72°02'·8 bearing N, what is the latitude? Index
    error −1'·6, ht of eye 6 ft.

2. On February 15th when in 46°40' S 167°20' E by DR an afternoon sun
    sight was taken when the chronometer, which was 3^m 45^s slow,
    showed 5^h 50^m 5^s. The sextant alt. LL was 21°18'·3, index error − 3'·5,
    ht of eye 10 ft. Find the CP, intercept and bearing, ready for plotting.

3. The position by DR is 47°20' S 168°15' E. The morning sun sight on
    August 30th gave:
    　CP 47° S 168°30'·4 E, Intercept, AWAY 16·5, bearing 047°
    At midday the yacht had sailed 23 M by log, Co 035° T when a sun
    mer. alt. gave the latitude as 47°00'·5 S. What was the OP then?

4. Find the times of morning civil twilight and sunrise, and of sunset
    and end of civil twilight on February 16th when in 42° N 65° W.
    GMT is required.

5. The yacht is bound for Wellington, N.Z., from Sydney. The EP is 40° S
    169° E. Soon after dawn on February 15th the ship's clock is found to
    have stopped due to the omission to wind it up. The chronometer,
    which has an error 6^m 45^s fast, shows 6^h 28^m. What should the ship's

clock be set to, and what should be the zone number entered at the head of the time column in the log book?

6. The yacht is on passage from Honolulu to Singapore and is in 15° N 179°45′ W by DR. The last log entry reads

$$\frac{Z+12}{2345}$$

Sept. 10th

She should shortly cross the date line. How will the first log book entry after midnight appear, and how should ship's clock and chronometer be dealt with?

7. An evening twilight sight of POLARIS is taken on August 29th when in 38°20′ N 136°15′ W by DR. The chronometer (which is correct) shows $3^h 54^m 32^s$ when the sextant alt. of Polaris is 38°07′·4, index error − 5′·0 and ht of eye 10 ft. What is the latitude?

8. When in 42° S 163°30′ E by DR at morning twilight on August 31st JUPITER is observed, sextant alt. 26°43′·8 when the chronometer (which is correct) shows $6^h 53^m 49^s$. Index error is 1′·6 on the arc and ht of eye is 6 ft. Give the CP, intercept and bearing, ready for plotting.

9.a Dawn twilight sights of stars are to be taken on May 20th when in 42° S 160°30′ E by DR. Using 'Selected Stars' Vol. 1, list the three stars marked as being best placed in azimuth which should be available then, and give their approximate altitudes and bearings.

b These three stars are observed in their listed order:
Star No. 1 at 19-52-13 GMT. Sextant Alt. 51°47′·9
Star No. 2 at 19-52-46 GMT. Sextant Alt. 22°19′·7
Star No. 3 at 19-53-12 GMT. Sextant Alt. 28°28′·2
IE 1′·3 OFF the arc, ht of eye 8 ft.
Find the respective CPs, intercepts and bearings ready for plotting.

Chapter 6

10. Evening sights of two stars are taken on August 29th when in DR 34°10′ S 152° E. Vol. 1, Selected Stars, is not available. Using Vol. 2 find the respective CPs, intercepts and bearings, ready for plotting:

  SPICA   at 07-53-54 GMT. Sextant Alt. 41°52′·9

  ARCTURUS   07-54-32 GMT. Sextant Alt. 27°34′·8

Index error was 4′·2 on the arc, ht of eye 8 ft.

11. About dawn twilight on August 30th when in 42°40′ S 162°15′ E the MOON's upper limb is observed, 26°34′·6 when the chronometer (which is correct) shows 6^h 55^m 12^s. Index error is −1′·4, ht of eye 6 ft. Find the CP, intercept and bearing, ready for plotting.

12.a On February 17th when in 40° S 158° E by DR the MOON is to be observed at meridian passage to provide the latitude. At what time, GMT, will she be on the meridian of the DR?

  b If the sextant alt. of MOON's LL was then 33°31′·0, what was the observed latitude? IE − 2′·5, ht of eye 6 ft.

13. When in 34°10′ S 152° E, simultaneous evening star sights are taken, which give these results:

  ALTAIR   CP 34° S 152°12′·1 E Intercept AWAY   8·5, bearing 058°

  SPICA   34° S 152°35′·8 E Intercept TO   17·9, bearing 287°

  ARCTURUS   34° S 152°06′·0 E Intercept AWAY 12·0, bearing 323°

Plot, and give the OP.

14. When in 39°20′ S 143°30′ E a compass check by sun's azimuth was carried out in the forenoon of February 16th at 21-54-13 GMT. The bearing of the sun by steering compass was 085° C. What was the total error of the compass, and if variation locally was 12° E, what was the deviation on the ship's heading at the time?

15.a On February 15th the yacht's position by DR was 48° S 105° W when the sun was observed at meridian passage. The sextant alt. was LL 54°21′·3 bearing N. Index error was − 2′·3 and ht of eye 8 ft. Log reading 474·0 M.

An afternoon sun sight was taken the same day when the chronometer (which was correct) showed 10^h 54^m 2^s. The sextant alt. LL was 31°48'·0. Log reading 497 M. Co made good since midday, 104° T, index error and ht of eye as before. Plot the OP.

b No sights could be taken until the late afternoon of the following day, February 16th. The yacht had then sailed 132 M by log, Co 135° T and it was estimated that a current of $\frac{1}{2}$ kn had been setting 140°, drift 13 M. Simultaneous sights of SUN and MOON were:

MOON at 00-52-27 GMT. Sextant Alt. Upper Limb 19°52'·9
SUN at 00-53-12 GMT. Sextant Alt. Lower Limb 10°46'·7
IE − 2'·3, ht of eye 8 ft. Find the OP.

c As the last OP placed the yacht some distance from the EP further simultaneous sights were taken at dusk the same day, after the yacht had sailed a further 11·5 M Co 135° T:
(Use Vol. 1, Selected Stars for the three stars.)

Souhail at 02-53-04 GMT. Sextant Alt. 56°31'·4
ACHERNAR 02-53-46 GMT. Sextant Alt. 53°15'·0
ALDEBARAN 02-54-17 GMT. Sextant Alt. 21°09'·6
SATURN 02-54-50 GMT. Sextant Alt. 16°00'·4
IE − 2'·3, ht of eye 8 ft. What was the OP then?

16. A non-stop passage from Durban to Dunedin, N.Z., is under consideration. Using Great Circle Diagram No 5029 (or any other method) work out a composite great circle route which goes no further south than 55° S. Give Lat./Long. of intermediate points at 10° intervals of long., and total mileage involved. Start from 30° S 32° E to a point 48° S 165° E.

17. The radio is fading and the last radio time checks possible before it finally fades are:
April 10th Chron. error 4^m 6^s slow
April 18th Chron. error 3^m 46^s slow.
A sight is taken on May 4th when the time by chronometer is 04^h 18^m 13^s. What is the GMT to use for the sight?

Answers 1

1975 May 20ᵗ DR. 48°20'N. 14°30'W

Mer: Pass: 11-56 LMT
DR.Long: in time, 14°30'W + 58
12-54 GMT at D.R.

Sextant Alt: L.L. 61°30'.6 bng S
I.E. -2'.0
Dip -2.4   -4.4
61° 26.2

Corn: +15.4
TRUE ALT: 61°41.6 S
from 90°
T.Z.D. 28° 18'.4 N (Name reversed)
Dec: 12ʰ 19°54.4N.
d,+0.5 54ᵐ +0.5
19°54.9 N
LAT: 48° 13'.3 N.

2

1975 May 19th at 15-54-33 GMT. DR. 49°50'N. 4°20'W. I.E -2'·0, HE 6 ft.

[USING Vol: 3, A.P. 3270 OR H.O. 249]

GHA 15^h   45° 53'·9   Dec: N 19° 43'·2
Incr: 54^m 33^s   13° 38.3   d, +0·5   + 0·5
                    59° 32'·2   N 19° 43'·7

C.P. Long: W − 4° 32·2
L.H.A.   55°   Sextant Alt: L.L. 36° 58'·8
C.P. Lat: N 50'   I.E. −2'·0
Dec: N 19° 44'   Dip −2·4   − 4·4
                                                  36° 54'·4

      Hc   36° 44'   Corn: + 14·7
d, +45   + 33   TRUE ALT: 37° 09·1
TAB: ALT: 37° 17'   TAB: "   37° 17·0
                    360°   Intercept, AWAY   7·9
            Z   − 105°
                255° = Z m.

CP 50° N 4°32'·2 W Intercept AWAY 7·9, bearing 255°

[OR, using N.P. 401 on H.O. 229]

    LHA   55°
C.P. Lat: N 50°
Dec: N 19° 43'·7

        Hc   36° 43'·6
d, +45·1   40 =   29·2
            5·1 =   3·7   TRUE ALT: (above) 37° 09'·1
TAB: ALT: 37° 16'·5   TAB: "   37° 16·5
                                Intercept: AWAY   7·4
                    360°
            Z − 104°·9
                255°·1   Z m.

2.   See Ocean Yacht Navigator Chapters 4 and 5, pp 41, 45.

3

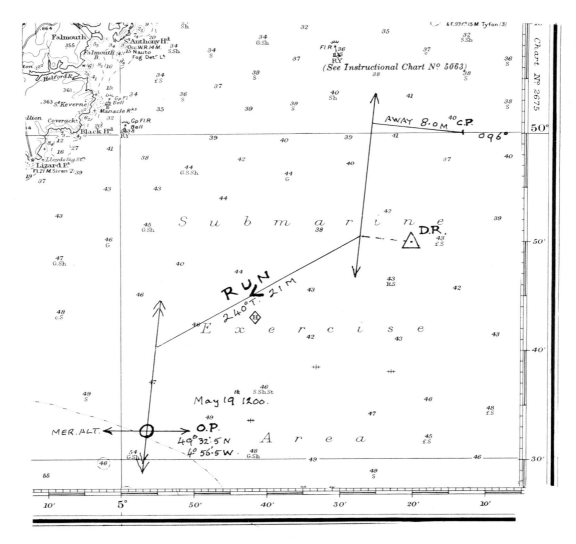

Here is an alternative, and rather more elegant way of plotting a position from a transferred PL.
The CP is plotted as usual. The 'run' is then plotted on from the CP. The intercept and its PL is plotted from the end of the 'run', and the PL is marked as a transferred PL.
This saves one operation

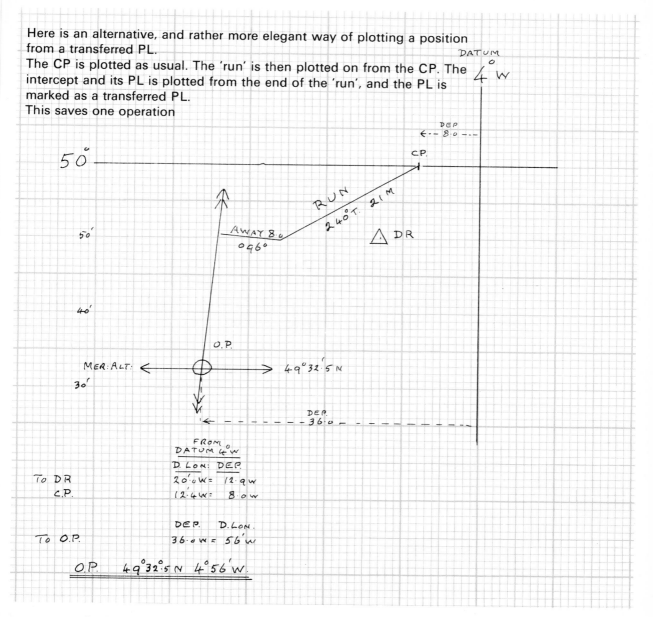

Answers 1

4   August 29th in DR 52° N 3° E.

	C. Twilight	Sun Rise	Sun Set	C. Twilight
	04 31	05 07	18 53	19 29
Long. in time, 3° E	− 12	− 12	− 12	− 12
GMT at DR	04 19	04 55	18 41	19 17

5   As the DR position reaches about $7\frac{1}{2}°$ W, $22\frac{1}{2}°$ W, $37\frac{1}{2}°$ W, and each successive 15° further W, the ship's clock should be put BACK one hour. A line should be drawn across the log book and the new Zone number entered. Between $7\frac{1}{2}°$ W and $22\frac{1}{2}°$ W this should be Z + 1, the number being increased as each zone is entered.
The chronometer, or timepiece being used as such, should *never* be altered (except to correct a substantial error, fast or slow).

6   As at midnight on the night she crosses 180°, a line is drawn across the log book under the last entry. Z + 12 is altered to Z − 12, the date ADVANCED by two days, that is, one day is "lost".
The ship's clock is left UNALTERED, and chronometer is of course, left undisturbed, e.g.

$$
\begin{array}{l}
\phantom{\text{Aug. 5th }}Z + 12 \\
\text{Aug. 5th } \underline{23\ \ 30 } \\
\phantom{\text{Aug. 5th }}Z - 12 \\
\text{Aug. 7th } 00\ \ 15.
\end{array}
$$

4.   See Ocean Yacht Navigator p 75 and Nautical Almanac p 257.

5.   See Ocean Yacht Navigator Chapter 9, p 67 and Nautical Almanac pp 262–5.

6.   See Ocean Yacht Navigator Chapter 9, p 71 and Nautical Almanac p 261.

7 1975 May 19th at 03^h 55^m GMT. DR 50°N. 5°45'W. IE −4.3, HE 8ft.

GHA Aries 03^h 281° 10.1
         55^m 13° 47.3
              294° 57.4
   DR Long: W −   5° 45.0.
    LHA γ   289° 12.4

Sextant Alt: POLARIS   49° 49.0
           IE −4.3
           Dip −2.7   −7.0
                  49° 42.0.
         Corn: −0.8
                 49° 41.2
   Polaris Corr'n A$_0$ 1° 10.6
             A$_1$ .6
             A$_2$ .3.
                50° 52.7
                − 1°
     LAT: 49° 52.7

---

8 1975 Aug. 30th 04-55-17 GMT. DR. 50°20'N. 2°50'W. IE −4.0, HE 8ft.

GHA JUPITER. 04^h 14° 38.9   **Dec** N 8° 00.5
         55-17   13° 49.3   d-0.1   −0.1
     v. 2.6   2.4   N 8° 00.4
           28° 30.6
   C.P. Long: W − 2° 30.6
     L.H.A.   26°
   C.P. Lat: N 50°
     Dec: N 8° 00'

Sext. Alt. JUPITER   42° 37.7
         IE −4.0
         Dip −2.7   −6.7
               42° 31.0
      Corn: −1.1
   TRUE ALT: 42° 29.9
      TAB: "   42° 45.0
   Intercept: AWAY 15.1

Hc   42° 45'   360°
d, +55   −   Z −144
TAB: ALT: 42° 45'   216° = Zm.

OR, using N.P.401 or H.O.229.

LHA   26°   Hc   42° 44.6   TRUE ALT: 42° 29.9
Lat: N 50°   d,+55.4, 50=   .3   TAB: "   42° 44.9
Dec: N 8° 00.4   5.   5.4=   −   **Intercept:** AWAY 15.0
           TAB: ALT: 42° 44.9   360°
                               Z − 143.8
                               216.2   Zn.

7. See Ocean Yacht Navigator Chapter 7, p 58 and Nautical Almanac pp 256, 274–6.

8. See Ocean Yacht Navigator Chapter 10, p 73.

Answers 1

Using Marcq St Hilaire Haversine/Cosine Formula

1975 Aug 30ᵗʰ 04-55-17 GMT.   DR 50°20'N. 2°50'W.   IE −4.0, HE 8 ft.

J U P I T E R.

GHA. 04ʰ 14°38.9   Dec: N 8°00'.5
    55-17 13°49.3   d−0.1   −0.1
    V. 2.6   2.4   N 8° 00.4
              28° 30.6

DR. Long: W − 2° 50.
    LHA   25°40.6   Log Hav: 8.69349
DR. Lat: N 50° 20.0 Log Cos. 9.80504
    Dec: N 8° 00.4 Log Cos. 9.99575
                       Log Hav: 8.49428
               = Nat. Hav: .03121   Sextant Alt: 42° 37.7
Lat:∼ Dec: 42°19.6 →   "   " .13034   IE −4.0
                       −   "   16155   Dip−2.7   −6.7
                                                   42° 31.0
                = C.Z.D. 47°23.9   Conn: −1.1
                  from 90°   TRUE ALT: 42° 29.9
          CALC: ALT: 42°36.1   CALC: " 42° 36.1
                                     Intercept. AWAY 6.2

Table A = S 2.50
      B = N .33
      C   S 2.17 in Lat. 50° = S 35.8 W = *Bearing* 215.8°

44

9 1975 May 21st at dawn. DR. 50°10'N. 6°W.   IE −4'·0, HE 6 ft.

<u>PRE-PLAN</u> C. Twilight a.m. 0328 LMT.

DR Long: in time, 6°W + 24

$\overline{\qquad 0352 \text{ GMT at DR.}}$

GHA. Aries 03^h 283° 08'·3   ⎧ Mirfak   21° 55'   037°
        52^m 13° 02·1   ⎨ ALTAIR   48° 21   169°
           296° 10·4   ⎩ ARCTURUS 23° 21   273°
DR Long: W − 6°
LHA ♈ 290° 10·4 (<u>use 290°</u>.)

<u>SIGHTS TAKEN</u>:

		<u>MIRFAK</u>	<u>ALTAIR</u>	<u>ARCTURUS</u>
at GMT		03-53-44	03-54-20	03-55-05.
GHA Aries	03^h	283° 08'·3	283° 08'·3	283° 08'·3
	53-44	13° 28·2	54-20 13° 37·2	55-05 13° 48·5
		296° 36·5	296° 45·5	296° 56·8
C.P.s Long: W −		5° 36·5	− 5° 45·5	− 5° 56·8
LHA ♈		291°	291°	291°
C.P.s Lat:	N	50°	N 50°	N 50°
TAB: ALT: Hc		22° 19'	48° 28'	22° 42'
Zn		037°	170°	273°

<u>Sextant Alt</u>:   22° 33'·8   48° 17'·3   22° 53'·2
     IE −4'·0
     Dip −2·4   −6·4   −6·4   −6·4
          22° 27·4   48° 10·9   22° 46·8
     Corn: −2·3   − 0·9   − 2·3
 TRUE ALT: 22° 25·1   48° 10·0   22° 44·5
 TAB: " 22° 19·0   48° 28·0   22° 42·0
Intercept: TO 6·1   AWAY 18·0   TO   2·5

9. See Ocean Yacht Navigator Chapter 10, p 74.

10   Aug 31ˢᵗ in DR 50°20'N. 3°10'W.   I.E. -1.3, H.E 8 ft.

<table>
<tr><td></td><td>ALTAIR.</td><td>ARCTURUS.</td></tr>
<tr><td>GMT</td><td>19-53-12.</td><td>19-53-41.</td></tr>
</table>

	ALTAIR	ARCTURUS
SHA ✱	62° 35.6 Dec: N 8°48.5	146° 21.7 Dec: N 19°18.7
GHA ♈ 19ʰ	264° 19.9	264° 19.9
Incr:	13° 20.2	13° 27.5
	340° 15.7	424° 09.1
		−360°
		64° 09.1
CPs Long: W	− 3° 15.7	− 3° 09.1
LHA ✱	337°	61°
CP Lat:	N 50°	N 50°
Dec:	N 8° 48'	N 19° 19'

	ALTAIR		ARCTURUS	
Hc	43° 50'		Hc 32° 58'	360°
d, +56	+ 45		d, +44 +14	Z −100
TAB: ALT:	44° 35' Z 148° = Zn		33° 12' Z	260° = Zn.

ALTAIR		ARCTURUS	
Sextant Alt:	44° 30'.0	33° 16'.8	
I.E. −1.3			
Dip −2.7	−4.0	−4.0	
	44° 26.0	33° 12.8	
Conn:	−1.0	− 1.5	
TRUE ALT:	44° 25.0	33° 11.3	
TAB:	44° 35.0	33° 12.0	
Intercept:	AWAY 10.0	AWAY 0.7	

OR Using N.P.401 or HO 229

	ALTAIR			ARCTURUS	
Hc	43° 49'.9	TRUE ALT: 44° 25.0	Hc 32° 57'.6	TRUE ALT: 33° 11.3	
d, +56.2, 50 =	40.0	TAB: " 44° 34.9	d, 44 44 0 = 12.6	TAB: " 33° 11.6	
6.2 =	5.0	Intercept. AWAY 9.9	4.4 = 1.4	Intercept: AWAY 0.3	
	44° 34.9		33° 11.6		
		Z 147°.6 = Zn.		360°	
				Z − 99.7	
				260°.3 = Zn.	

10. See Ocean Yacht Navigator Chapter 10, p 78.

Using Marcq St Hilaire Haversine/Cosine Formula

1975 Aug 31ˢᵗ   DR 50°20'N. 3°10'W.   I.E. −1'3, HE 8 ft.

	ALTAIR.		ARCTURUS.
at GMT	19-53-12.		19-53-41.

	ALTAIR		ARCTURUS	
SHA ✱	62°35'6 Dec: N 8°48'5		146°21'7 Dec: N 19°18'7	
GHA ♈ 19ʰ	264° 19.9		264° 19.9	
Incr: 53-12	13° 20.2	53-41	13° 27.5	
	340° 15.7		424° 09.1	
DR. Long: W−	3° 10.0		− 3° 10.0	
			420° 59.1	
			− 360°	

	ALTAIR				ARCTURUS		
					60° 59'1	Log H	9.41094
LHA ✱	337°05'7	Log Hav:	8.59577				
DR. Lat:	N 50° 20.0	Log Cos.	9.80504	N 50° 20.0	Log C	9.80504	
Dec:	N 8° 48.5	Log Cos.	9.99485	N 19° 18.7	Log C	9.97486	
		Log Hav:	8.39566		Log H.	9.19084	
		= Nat.Hav.	.02487		= Nat.H.	.15518	
Lat ∼ Dec:	41° 31.5 →	" "	.12567	31° 01.3 →	" "	.07151	
		" "	.15054			.22669	

	ALTAIR		ARCTURUS
C.Z.D.	45° 39'6		56° 51'8
from	90°		90°
CALC: ALT:	44° 20'4		33° 08'2

	ALTAIR			ARCTURUS	
Sextant Alt:	44° 30'0			33° 16'8	
I.E. −1'3					
Dip −2.7	−4.0			−4.0	
	44° 26.0			33° 12.8	
Corn:	−1.0			− 1.5	
TRUE ALT:	44° 25.0			33° 11.3	
CALC: "	44° 20.4			33° 08.2	
Intercept:	**TO 4.6**			TO 3.1	

Azimuth: TABLE A = S 2.84   A = S .66
          B = N .40   B = N .40
          C, S 2.44 in Lat: 50°   C S .26 in Lat: 50°
             = S 33° E   = S 80°.5 W
             = 147°   = 260°.5   47

11 MOON. 1975 May 19ᵗʰ 16-53-22 GMT. DR. 50°20'N. 2°50'W.

I.E. −4'·0, HE 8 ft

GHA Moon 16ʰ 313°01'·8   Dec: N 1°23'·4   H.P. 59'·5
   Incr: 53-22   12° 44·0   d−12·9 −11·5
   V. 10·2   9·1   N 1° 11'·9
             325°54·9
C.P. Long: W − 2° 54·9   Sext. Alt. MOON L.L. 30°51'·7
   LHA   323°   IE −4'·0
C.P. Lat: N 50°   Dip −2·7 −6·7
   Dec: N 1° 12'   30° 45·0
                    Corn: 58·6
     Hc   31° 47'   H.P. 59'·5   7·0
  d, + 53 + 11.   TRUE ALT: 31°50·6
  TAB. ALT: 31° 58'   TAB: "   31° 58·0
                Intercept: AWAY 7·4
    Z 135° = Zn.

OR, Using N.P. 401 or H.O. 229.

   LHA 323°
   Lat: N 50°
   Dec: N 1° 11'·9

     Hc 31° 46'·7   TRUE ALT: 31° 50'·7 (above)
d, + 53·4, 50 = 10·0   TAB: "   31° 57·4.
       3·4 = 0·7   Intercept AWAY 6·9
TAB. ALT: 31° 57·4

    Z 134°·9 = Zn.

11. See Ocean Yacht Navigator Chapter 10, p 80.

Using Marcq St Hilaire Haversine/Cosine Formula

1975 May 19th 16-53-22 GMT. DR 50°20'N. 2°50'W. I.E. -4'.0, HE 8 ft.

MOON.

GHA 16[h] 313° 01.8 Dec: N 1° 23'.4   H.P. 59'.5
    53-22.   12° 44.0 d -12.9 -11.5
    V. 10.2   9.1   N 1° 11'.9
         325° 54.9
D.R. Long: W - 2° 50.0
    LHA. 323° 04.9   Log Hav: 9.00110
D.R. Lat: N 50° 20.0 Log Cos. 9.80504
    Dec: N 1° 11.9   Log Cos. 9.99990.
                     Log Hav. 8.80604
                        = Nat. " .06398   Sext. Alt. MOON L.L. 30° 51.7
Lat: ~ Dec: 49° 08.1 →   " " .17286   I E   -4.0
                         " " .23684   Dip -2.7 -6.7
                                                          30° 45.0
                    = C.Z.D. 58° 14.6   Corn: 58.6
                     from   90°   H.P. 59.5 7.0
                    CALC: ALT: 31° 45.4   TRUE ALT: 31° 50.6
                                                  CALC: " 31° 45.4
                                                 Intercept: To 5.2

Azimuth - TABLE A = 51.60
                 B = N .04
                 C   51.56 = S 45° E
                            = 135°

49

12

1975 May 19th DR. 56° 50' N. 9° 30' W.

Moon Mer: Pass: 19.15 GMT at 0°
Correction for Long: 9°30'W + 1   ×
                  19.16

Long: in time, 9°30'W + 38.
                   19 54 GMT at DR ⊞

× Correction for long:
19^D = 1915
20^D = 2006
∴ 1 day (360°) = + 51^m
∴ 9°30' = 51 × $\frac{9.5}{360}$ = 1.3, say 1^m

(Or by Table 11, p xxxii in Nautical Almanac, last buff page.)

Sextant Alt: MOON U.L. 33° 05'.9 bng: S.
       I.E. −3.3
       Dip −2.7   −6.0
                32° 59.9
      Corn: 57.5
H.P. 59.5 (U.L)   4.6
               34° 02.0
    for U.L.   −30.0
TRUE ALT: 33° 32.0   S
    from   90°
    T.Z.D.   56° 28.0   N
Dec: 19^h 0° 44'.5 N
d −13.0   54^m   −11.8   0° 32.7 N.
LAT: 57° 00'.7   N.

⊞ _Alternative method, to nearest second_

Required LHA Moon − 0°
   DR Long: W + 9° 30'
     = GHA   9° 30'
        + 360°
       369° 30'
       356° 29'.5 = 19^h
remainder   13° 00.5
   v. 10.2   9.1
          12° 51'.4 = 53^m 53^s

PROOF
GHA Moon 19^h 356° 29'.5
2uer: 53-53   12° 51.4
v. 10.2   9.1
          369° 30.0
          −360
   GHA   9° 30'.0
D.R. Long W − 9° 30'.0
     ∴ LHA   0°
   = on Merid: of the D.R.

Time on Merid: of D.R. 19-53-53 GMT.

12. See Ocean Yacht Navigator Chapter 10, p 82.

13

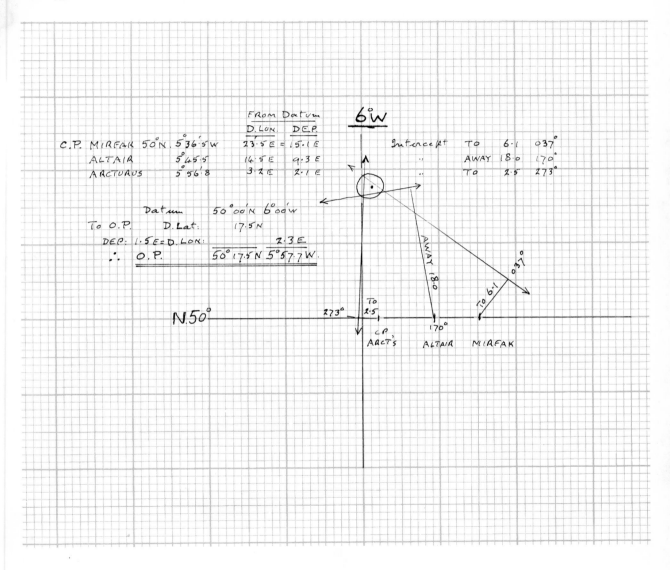

		FROM Datum				
		D. LON.	DEP.			
C.P. MIRFAK 50°N. 5°36'·5 W		23·5 E = 15·1 E		Intercept	TO	6·1	037°
ALTAIR 5°45'·5		14·5 E	9·3 E	"	AWAY 18·0	170°
ARCTURUS 5°56'·8		3·2 E	2·1 E	"	TO	2·5	273°

Datum 50°00'N 6°00'W

To O.P. D. Lat: 17·5 N

DEP: 1·5 E = D. LON: 2·3 E

∴ O.P. 50° 17·5 N 5° 57·7 W.

6°W

N.50°

273°

To 2·5

C.P. ARCT'S

170°

ALTAIR

MIRFAK

AWAY 18·0

To 6·1

037°

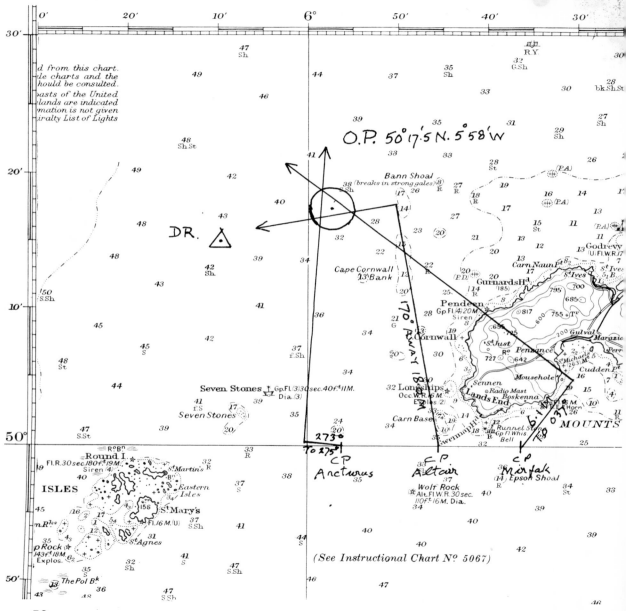

14

Compass check by Sun's Azimuth. Bearing 099°c on 1975 May 19th at 07-53-15 GMT in DR. 49°50'N. 4°20'W.

GHA.	285° 54'·1	Dec:	N 19° 38'·9
Incr:	13° 18·8	d+0·5	+ 0·4
	299° 12·9		N 19° 39·3
DR. Long: W —	4° 20·0		
L.H.A	294° 52·9		

Use L H A 295°
    Lat: N 50°
    Dec: N 19° 39'

$$Z = \underline{96° = Z m}.$$

Bearing of sun	096° T
Variation	+ 7° W
	103° Mag:
Compass	099° ·C
∴ Deviation	4° E on yacht's heading at the time.

Var'n   7° W
Dev'n   4° E
∴ TOTAL ERROR = 3° W

15

1975 May 19th 07-53-15 GMT. DR 49°50'N. 4°20'W. I.E. -3'·0, HE. 8 ft.

GHA 07^h 285° 54'·1 Dec: N 19°38'·9
  53-15   13° 18·8   d, +0·5   + 0·4
        299° 12·9   N 19°39'·3

C.P. Long: W - 4° 12·9
   LHA   295°
C.P. Lat: N 50°
  Dec: N 19°39'

       Hc   30°25'
   d, + 44   + 29·
  TAB: ALT: 30° 54'

      Z   96° = Zn.

Sextant Alt: L.L.   30°37'·3
     I.E.   -3'·0
     Dip -2·7   - 5·7
              30° 31'·6
     Conn: + 14·4
  TRUE ALT: 30° 46·0
     TAB: "   30° 54·0·
 Intercept: AWAY 8·0

RUN: 240°T, 21 M

     New DR.   49°37'N. 4°55'W.

     Mer: Pass: 11 56   LMT.
   DR. Long: 4°55'W + 20
             12 16   GMT at DR.

     MER: ALT: Sextant Alt: L.L. 59° 59'·5 brg S
                 I.E & Dip   - 5·7
                       59° 53·8
             Conn: + 15·4
          TRUE ALT: 60° 09·2   S
               from   90°
            T.Z.D.   29° 50'·8   N.
          Dec: 12^h 19°41'·6 N
    d, +0·5   16^m + 0·1   19° 41·7   N.
          LAT: 49°32'·5 N.

    O.P.   49°32'·5 N. 4°56'W.

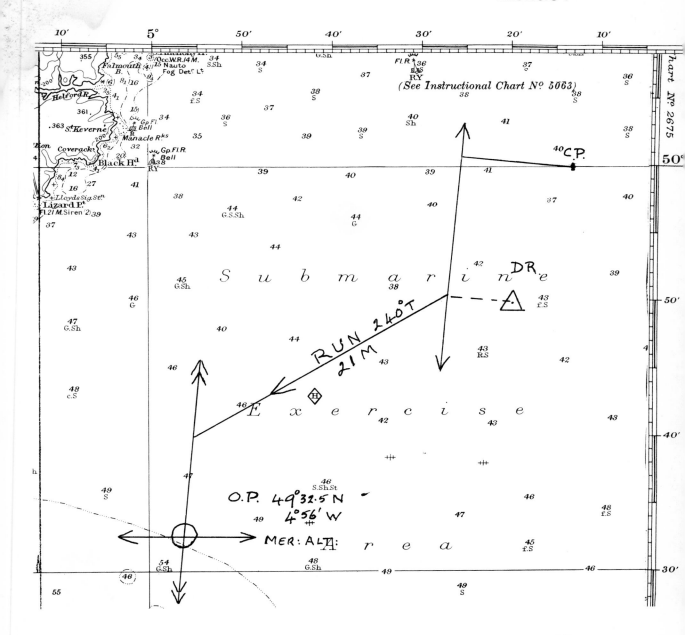

15.a   *Using Marcq St Hilaire Haversine/Cosine Formula*

1975 May 19ᵗʰ 07-53-15 GMT.   DR 49°50'N. 4°20'W.   I.E.-3'0, Ht E 8 ft.

```
G H A 07ʰ   285° 54'·1    Dec N 19° 38'·9
    53-15     13° 18·8     d +0·5      + 0·4
            299° 12·9               N 19° 39'·3
DR. Long: W—   4° 20·0                          Sextant Alt: L.L. 30° 37'·3
     L H A.  294° 52·9   L.H  9·46184              I.E. -3·0
DR. Lat: N 49° 50·0     L.C  9·80957              Dip -2·7        - 5·7
    Dec: N 19° 39·3     L.C  9·97393                            30° 31·6
                        L.H  9·24534              Corr:          + 14·4
                           = N.H.  ·17593.        TRUE ALT: 30° 46·0
  Lat ~ Dec: 30° 10·7 →    "    ·06776            CALC:  "    30° 50·3
                                 ·24369          Intercept: AWAY 4·3

                        = C Z D 59° 09'·7
                        from   90°
              CALC: ALT: 30° 50'·3

       TABLE  A = S ·58
              B = N ·39
              C    S ·19 = S 83° E = 097° Zn.

    RUN:  240°T  21 M.        New D.R. Long: 4° 56'W

        Mer: Pass: 1216 GMT at DR.

     Lat: as on previous Mer: Alt:  49° 32'·5 N.

        Per Plot:  O.P. 49° 32'·5 N. 4° 56'W.
```

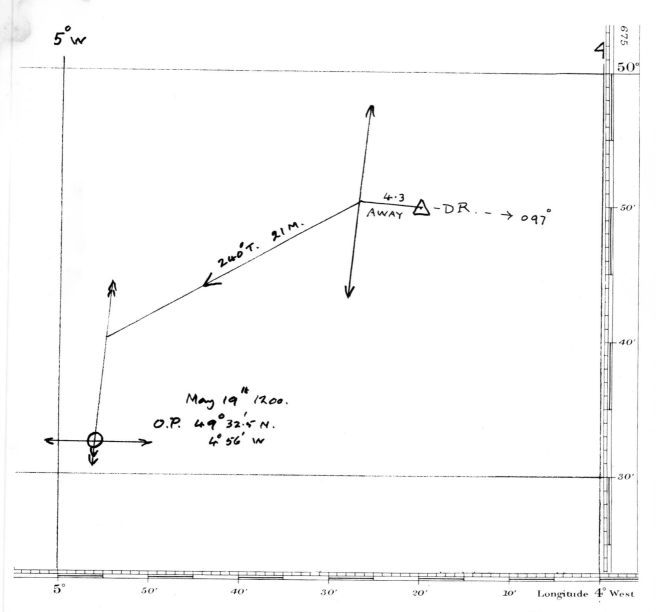

5° W

675

50°

4·3
AWAY — DR . — → 097°

50'

240° T. 21 M.

40'

May 19th 1200.
O.P. 49° 32·5 N.
4° 56' W

30'

5°   50'   40'   30'   20'   10'   Longitude 4° West

15.b

May 19ᵗ. midday O.P. 49°32'N. 4°56'W.

RUN : 292°T 48 M. new DR per plot, 49°51'N. 6°04'W.

	SATURN.	MOON	ARCTURUS	SPICA	REGULUS.
at GMT	20-52-10.	20-52-41	20-53-05	20-53-50	20-54-15.
GHA	69°53'2	N22°23·9	10°58'7 N0°31·4	♈176°52·0	♈176°52·0	♈176°52·0
Incr:	13°02·5		12°34·2 -12·9 -11·3	13°18·4	13°29·7	13°36·0
v.2·2	1·9	v.10·3 9·0	N0°20·1 SHA146°21·5	SHA★159°01·1	SHA★208°13·9.
	82°57·6		23°41·9	336°31·9	349°22·8	38°41·9
CP Long: W —	5°57·6		− 5°41·9	− 5°31·9	− 5°22·8	− 5°41·9·
LHA	77°		18°	331°	344°	33°
CP Lat:	N 50°	N 50°	N 50°	N 50°	N50°
Dec:	N 22°24'	N 0°20'	N 19°18'	S 11°02'	N 12°05'
Hc	24°54'	37°41'	51°21'	27°25'	43°22'
d,+43	+17	d+58. +19	d+52 +16	d−59 − 2	d+52 + 4
TAB: ALT:	25°11'	38°00'	51°37'	27°23'	43°26'
	360	360°			360
Z	− 85°	−157°			− 133
= Zn	275°	203°	133°	162°	227°
Sext: Alt:	25°21·1	LL 37°23·2	51°37'7	27°35'1	43°52'7
IE −3·0					
Dip −2·7	−5·7	−5·7	−5·7	−5·7	−5·7
	25°15·4	37°17·5	51°32·0	27°29·4	43°47·0
Conn:	−2·0	+55·2	− 0·8	− 1·9	− 1·0
		HP.59·5 + 6·9			
TRUE ALT:	25°13·4	38°19·6	51°31·2	27°27·5	43°46·0.
TAB: "	25°11·0	38°00·0	51°37·0	27°23·0	43°26·0
Intercept:	To 2·4	To 19·6	AWAY 5·8	To 4·5	To 20·0.

O.P. 49°46'N. 6°04'W.

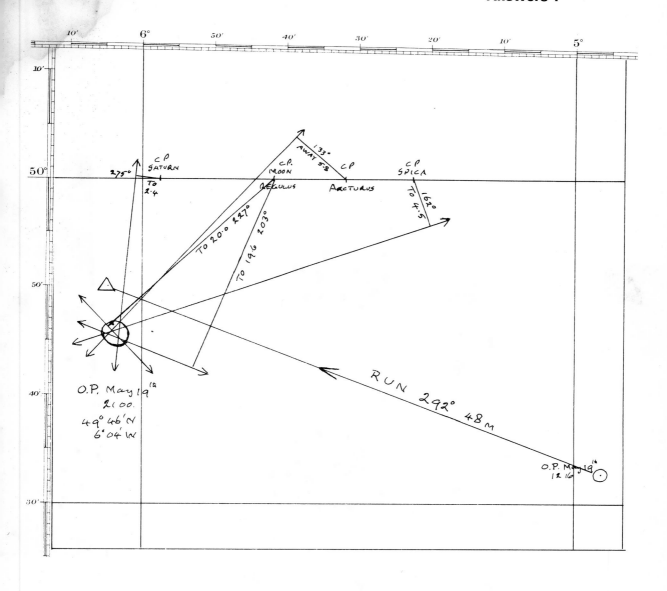

Using Marcq St Hilaire Haversine/Cosine Formula

RUN: 292° T. 48 M. NEW DR. 49° 51'N. 6° 05'W.

	SATURN	MOON.	ARCTURUS	SPICA	REGULUS.
GMT	20-52-10	20-52-41	20-53-05	20-53-50	20-54-15.
G 1+A	69°53'2 N 22°23'9	10°58·7 N 0°31'5	SHA 146°21'5. N19°18'5	159°01·1 S 11°02'2	208°13'9 N 12°05'2
Incr:	13°02·5	12°34·2 d-129-11·3	⋎ 176°52·0	⋎ 176°52·0	⋎ 176°52·0
v.2·2 1·9		v 10·3 9·0 N 0°20·2	13°18·4	13°29·7	13°36·0.
	82°57·6	23°41·9	336°31·9	349°22·8	398°41·9
DR. Long: W− 6°05·0	6°05·0	−6°05·0	−6°05·0	−6°05·0	−6°05·0
LHA	76°52·6 9·58712	17°36·9 8·37003	330°26·9 8·81321	343°17·8 8·32422	32°36·9 8·89677
DR Lat: N 49°51	9·80942	N 49°51 9·80942	N 49°51 9·80942	N 49°51 9·80942	N 49°51 9·80942
Dec: N 22°23·9	9·96593	N 0°20·2 9·99999	N 19°18·5 9·97686	S 11°02·2 9·99189	N 12°05·2 9·99026
	9·36247	8·17944	8·59749	8·12553	8·69645
	= ·23039	= ·01511	= ·03958	= ·01335	= ·04971
Lat~Dec: 27°27·1 → ·05630	49°30·8 → ·17536	30°32·5 → ·06937	60°53·2 → ·25673	37°45·8 → ·10473.	
	·28669	·19047	·10895	·27008	·15444
= CZD	64°44·8	51°45·2	38°32·8	62°37·4	46°17·0
from	90°	90°	90°	90°	90°
CALC: ALT:	25°15·2	38°14·8	51°27·2	27°22·6	43°43·0
Sextant Alt:	25°21·1	LL 37°23·2	51°37·7	27°35·1	43°52·7
IE −3·0 Dip −2·7	−5·7	−5·7	−5·7	−5·7	−5·7
	25°15·4	37°17·5	51°32·0	27°29·4	43°47·0.
Conn:	−2·0	+ 55·2.	− 0·8	−1·9	−1·0.
		1+P 59·5 + 6·9			
TRUE ALT	25°13·4	38°19·6	51°31·2	27°27·5	43°46·0.
CALC: "	25°15·2.	38°14·8	51°27·2.	27°22·6	43°43·0
Intercept:	AWAY. 1·8	TO 4·8	TO 4·0	TO 4·9	TO 3·0
Azimuths. Tables A =	S ·29	S 3·75	S 2·10	S 3·95	S 1·87
B =	N ·43	0·0	N ·71	S ·67	N ·39
C	N ·14	S 3·75.	S 1·39	S 4·62	S 1·48
=	N 84°9W	S 22°6 W	S 48°E	S 18°6 E	S 46°4W
=	275°·1	= 202°·6	= 132°	= 161°·4	= 226°·4

O.P. 49°46'N. 6°03'W.

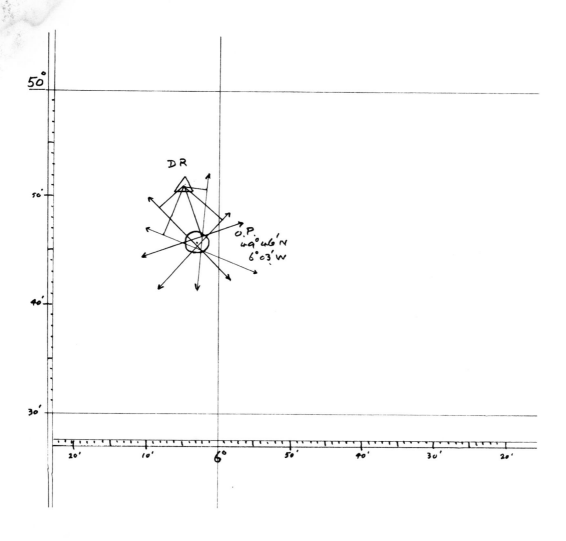

15.c

RUN: 264° 30 M.

New DR. 49°42'N. 6°50'W.

	POLARIS	MIRFAK	ALTAIR	ARCTURUS
May 20th. GMT.	03-52-00	03-52-13	03-52-55	03-53-25
GHA. ARIES	282° 09'.2	282° 09'.2	282° 09'.2	282° 09'.2
	13° 02.1	13° 05.4	13° 15.9	13° 23.4
	295° 11.3	295° 14.6	295° 25.1	295° 32.6
DR. Long. W-	6° 50.0	CP. - 6° 14.6	- 6° 25.1	- 6° 32.6
LHA	288° 21.3	289°	289°	289°
		CP. N 50°	N 50°	N 50°
		Hc 21°32'	Hc 48°13'	Hc 23°59'
		Zn 036°	Zn 168°	Zn 272°
Sextant Alt:	49° 33.4	21° 10.4	48° 37.1	24° 15.6
I.E. -3.0				
Dip -2.7	- 5.7	- 5.7	- 5.7	- 5.7
	49° 27.7	21° 04.7	48° 31.4	24° 09.9
Corrn:	- 0.8	- 2.5	- 0.9	- 2.2
TRUE ALT:	49° 26.9	TRUE 21° 02.2	48° 30.5	24° 07.7
A_0	1° 10.6	TAB: 21° 32.0	48° 13.0	23° 59.0
A_1	.6	AWAY 29.8	To 17.5	To 8.7
A_2	.5			
	50° 38.6			
	- 1°			
LAT.	49° 38.6			

O.P. 49°39'N. 6°47'W.

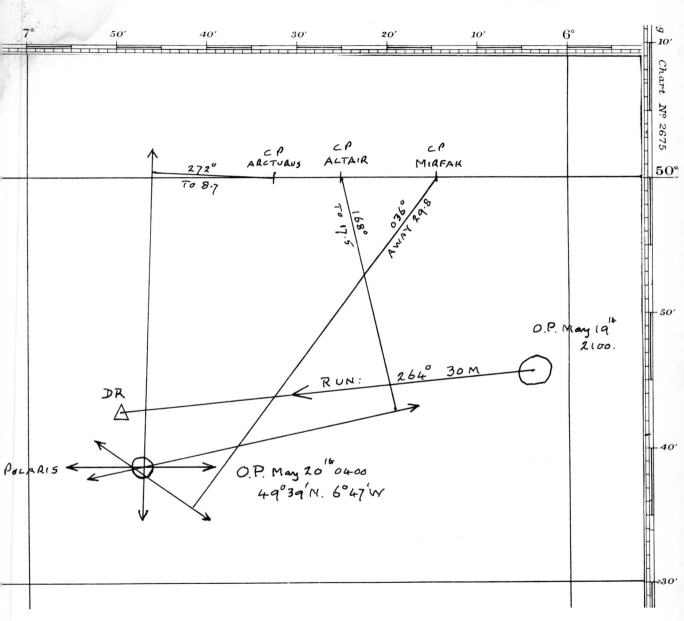

16   Position 32° N. 64° W   to   51° N 10° W.

<u>Great Circle Distance</u> *

Norie's Tables
P

```
                64° W
  D. Long.      10° W = 54°    log Hav    9 31409        450
  Lat            N 32°    log Cos   9 92842        225
  Lat            N 51°    log Cos   9 79887        244
                         log Hav    9 04138
                 ─────        = nat Hav   · 10999        435
  Lat ~ Lat.      19° →                · 02724
                         -  "      · 13723
                         =  43° 29'·2              440
```

=   2,609·2 Miles

<u>Rhumb line Distance</u>

```
                    Meridional Parts
  Lat   32° N        2,015·98                      ·42
  Lat   51° N        3,550·60                      145
           D.M.P.    1,534·62
```

```
  Long   64° W
         10° W
  D. Long  54°  × 60 =  3.240°  =   log 3 51055     162
  D.M.P.            1,534·62 =   log 3 18600        159
                            log tan 0 · 32455
                                  ↓
        32° N
  D Lat  51° N              log sec 0 36850         257
        19° × 60 = 1,140    log    3·05691         159
                            log   3 42541
```

=   2,663 Miles   161

<u>Great Circle track less than</u>
<u>Rhumb line by   54 Miles</u>

16.   See Ocean Yacht Navigator Chapter 14, p 109.

✳ ALTERNATIVELY, USING NP.401, 1+0229 or HD486

$$
\begin{aligned}
&\text{L.H.A. (= D.Long)} && 54° \\
&\text{Lat: (= Lat:)} && 51° \\
&\text{Dec: (= Lat:)} && 32°
\end{aligned}
\left.\vphantom{\begin{aligned}&\\&\\&\end{aligned}}\right\}
\quad
\begin{aligned}
&Hc = 46°30.7 \\
&= czD\ 43°29.3 \\
&= 2,609.3\ \text{Miles}
\end{aligned}
$$

17.   As final coincidence of the heavenly body and the horizon is made, the sextant should be 'rocked' or pivoted about the axis of the telescope, so that the body appears to rise and fall relative to the horizon. Adjustment by micrometer (or tangent screw) is made so that the body just touches the horizon at the lowest point of the rock or swing. If this is not done and the sextant is not vertical, the altitude obtained will be greater than the correct altitude.

The reference to Ocean Yacht Navigator at the foot of each answer applies equally to the similarly numbered answer in each section that now follows.

Answers 2

1   1975 Aug 29ᵗʰ   D.R. 38°N. 73°W.   I.E. −1'·3. HE 8 ft.

Mer: Pass: 12 01 LMT
DR Long: in time, 73°W + 4 52
                16 53 GMT at D.R.

$$
\begin{array}{lll}
\underline{\text{Sextant Alt:}} & \text{L.L.,} & 61°\,20'·2 \; \text{brg S.} \\
& \text{I.E.} -1'·3 \\
& \text{Dip} -2·7 & -4·0 \\
& & 61°\,16·2 \\
\text{Corn:} & & +15·4 \\
\text{TRUE ALT:} & & 61°\,31·6 \;\; \text{S} \\
\text{from} & & 90° \\
\text{T.Z.D.} & & 28°\,28·4 \;\; \text{N} \\
\underline{\text{Dec:}}\; 16^{h} & 9°\,25'·5 \,\text{N} \\
d, -0·9, 53^{m} & -0·8 & 9°\,24·7 \;\; \text{N} \\
\underline{\text{LAT:}} & & 37°\,53'·1 \;\; \text{N}
\end{array}
$$

2   1975 May 21st 09-54-52 GMT. D.R. 49°45'N. 6°50'W.

I E. −3'·0, H E. 5 ft.

GHA 09^h 315° 52'·5   Dec: N 20° 05'·3.
Iner: 54·52. 13° 43·0   d +0·5   + 0·5
329° 35·5   N 20° 05·8
C.P. Long: W − 6° 35·5
L.H.A. 323°
C.P. Lat: N 50°
Dec: N 20° 06'

Hc   48° 06'
d, +49   + 5
TAB: ALT: 48° 11'

Sextant Alt. L.L. 48° 06'·0
I.E. −3'·0
Dip −2·1   − 5·1
48° 00'·9
Conn: + 15·1
TRUE ALT: 48° 16·0
TAB: " 48° 11·0
Intercept: TO 5·0

Z 122° = Zm.

C.P. 50°N. 6° 35'·5 W. Intercept: TO 5·0, Bearing 122°.

OR   Using NP. 401 or HO. 229 or HD486.

LHA 323°
Lat: N 50°
Dec: N 20° 05'·8

Hc   48° 06'·4
d, +48·7   40 =   3·9
8·7 =   0·8
TAB: ALT: 48° 11·1

Zm = 122°·1

Answers 2

Using Marcq St Hilaire Haversine/Cosine Formula

May 21st. 09-54-52 GMT. DR 49°45'N. 6°50'W. I.E. –3.0 H.E. 5 ft.

GHA 09^h 315° 52'·5 Dec: N 20° 05'·3
54-52   13° 43·0   d +0·5   + 0·5.
          329° 35·5   N 20° 05·8.

D.R. Long: W – 6° 50·0.

L.H.A. 322° 45·5   log Hav 9·00841
D.R. Lat: N 49° 45·0   log Cos 9·81032
   Dec: N 20° 05·8   log Cos 9·97272.
                    log Hav. 8·79145.
                  = nat: Hav. ·06186.

Lat: ~ Dec: 29° 39·2. →   " ·06548.
                          " ·12734

                    = C.Z.D. 41° 48·8
                      from   90°
             Calc: Alt: 48° 11·2

Sextant Alt: L.L. 48° 06·0
   IE –3·0
   Dip –2·2   – 5·2
                 48° 00·8
   Corr: + 15·1
TRUE ALT: 48° 15·9
   CALC: " 48° 11·2
Intercept: TO   4·7

TABLE A = 51·60
       B = N ·60
       C,   51·00 = S 57° E
Bearing   = 123°

3

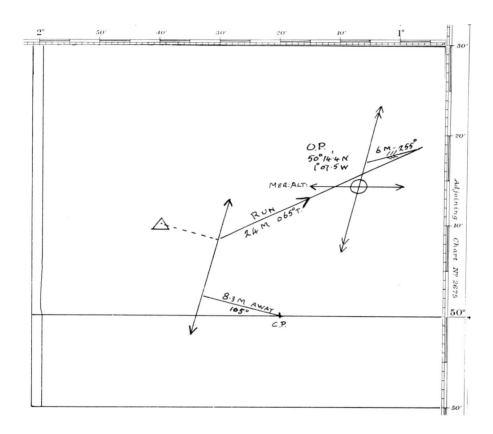

4 1975 May 20ᵗʰ D.R. 36° N. 12°W.

	a.m.		p.m		From Naut: Almanac		
	C.Twilight	Sunrise	Sunset	C.Twilight		C.T.	Sunrise
					N 35°	0425	0453
LMT 35°	0425	0453	1900	1928	N 40°	0410	0441
Corrⁿ fⁿ Lat: 36°·1°	−3	−2	+2	+3	Change of 5° =	−15	−12
LMT	0422	0451	1902	1931	∴ · 1° :	−3ᵐ	−2ᵐ
Long: in time, 12°W +	48	+48	+48	+48			
GMT at D.R.	0510	0539	1950	2019			

5 When the yacht reaches about 52½° W (the exact day is not vital), draw a line across the log book under the last entry, alter the Zone Time shown from Z + 4 to Z + 3, and ADVANCE the ship's clock by one hour.

The same action should be taken as she progressively crosses (about) 37½°, 22½°, and 7½° W. The chronometer should NOT of course be altered.

6 A line should be drawn across the log book after the last entry on June 14th. The Zone Time should be altered from Z − 12 to Z + 12 and the date brought forward UNALTERED, that is should be June 14th, i.e.

$$\text{June 14th } \frac{Z - 12}{23\ 45}$$

$$\text{June 14th } \frac{Z + 12}{00\ 15}$$

June 14ᵈ 23 45
Z − 12
GD 14ᵈ 11 45 GMT

June 14ᵈ 00 15
Z + 12
GD 14ᵈ 12 15 GMT

Thus, GMT has advanced by 30 minutes. The chronometer remains unaltered.

7   1975 Aug 31st at 21-53-00 GMT.   DR. 36°N. 44°W.   I.E. -3'0, HE 6 ft.

POLARIS.

G.H.A. Aries   21ʰ   294° 24'.9
    Incr: 53ᵐ   13° 17.2
                        307° 42.1
    DR Long: W - 44°
    L.H.A. Aries   263° 42'.1

    Sextant Alt: POLARIS   35° 56'.8
                 I.E. -3'0
                 Dip -2.4   - 5.4
                              35° 51'.4
              Corn: - 1.3
                              35° 50.1
    Polaris Corn: A₀   1° 30.5   (Interpolated)
                  A₁   0.5
                  A₂   0.9
                         37° 22.0
                        - 1°
            LAT: 36° 22'.0 N

8   1975 May 21ˢᵗ   20-53-18 GMT.   DR 50°05'N   6°10'W.   I.E. +1·4, HE 6 ft.

VENUS

GHA Venus 20ʰ   74°02'·4 Dec: N 25°20'·1
  Incr: 53-18   13°19.5   d -0·2   − 0·2
  V. − 0·6   −0·5   N25°19'·9
             87°21·4

C.P. Long: W − 6°21·4   Sextant Alt: VENUS   24°37'·5
  L.H.A.   81°   I.E. + 1·4
C.P. Lat: N 50°   Dip − 2·4   − 1·0
  Dec: N 25°20'   24°36·5

                              Corr: − 2·1
    Hc   24°31'   Add'nl Corn: + 0·1
 d, + 43   +14   TRUE ALT: 24°34·5
TAB: ALT: 24°45'   TAB: "   24°45·0
                       Intercept: AWAY 10·5

         360°
   Z − 80°
      280° = Zn

C.P.   50°N.   6°21·4 W   Intercept: AWAY 10·5, Bearing 280°.

9 1975 Aug 31st dusk sights in DR 50°20'N. 7°W

Advance Plan:　　　　C. Twilight 19 24 LMT
　　　　　　　　DR Long: in time, 7°w +　28
　　　　　　　　　　　　　　1952 GMT at DR.

GHA Aries 19^h　264° 19·9　　　Per Vol 1, AP3270.
　　52^m　　13° 02·1　　　　　　　　Alt.　　Zn.
　　　　　277° 22·0　　　　Mirfak　15°18'　025°
DR. Long: W –　7°　　　　ALTAIR　42 56　142°
LHA Ɣ　270° 22·0　　　ARCTURUS　36 06　257°
　　use 270° & Lat: 50°N

Sights taken:
　　　　　　　　1st　　　　　2nd　　　　　3rd
　　　　　　　MIRFAK　　　ALTAIR　　　ARCTURUS

	1st MIRFAK	2nd ALTAIR	3rd ARCTURUS
at GMT	19-52-28	19-53-12	19-53-41
GHA Aries 19^h	264° 19·9	264° 19·9	264° 19·9
52-28	13° 09·2	53-12 13° 20·2	53-41 13° 27·5
	277° 29·1	277° 40·1	277° 47·4
C.P. Long: W –	6° 29·1	– 6° 40·1	– 6° 47·4
LHA Ɣ	271°	271°	271°
C.P. Lat:	N 50°	N 50°	N 50°
Hc	15° 35'	43° 20'	35° 29'
Zn	026°	143°	257°
Sextant Alt: ✳	16° 06·3	43° 17·1	35° 12·0
IE – 1·3			
Dip – 2·7	– 4·0	– 4·0	– 4·0
	16° 02·3	43° 13·1	35° 8·0
Corr:	– 3·3	– 1·0	– 1·4
TRUE ALT	15° 59·0	43° 12·1	35° 6·6
TAB: "	15° 35·0	43° 20·0	35° 29·0
Intercept:	TO 24·0	AWAY 7·9	AWAY 22·4
C.P.	50°N 6°29·1'W	6°40'W	6°47·4 W
Bearing	026°	143°	257°

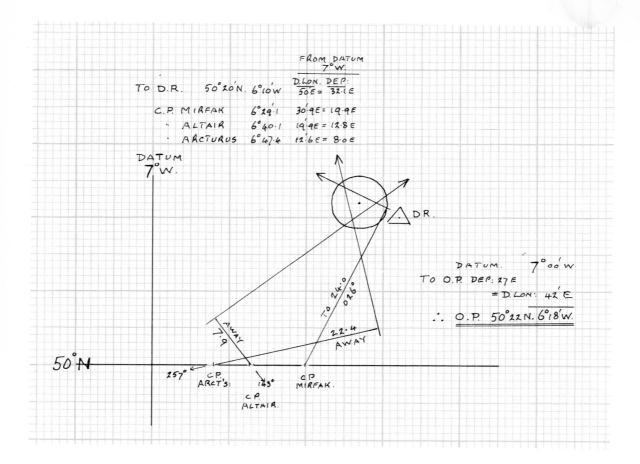

FROM DATUM
7° W.

		D.LON.	DEP:
TO D.R.	50°20'N. 6°10'W	50 E =	32.1 E
C.P. MIRFAK	6°29.1	30.9 E =	19.9 E
" ALTAIR	6°40.1	19.9 E =	12.8 E
" AARCTURUS	6°47.4	12.6 E =	8.0 E

DATUM
7° W.

DR.

DATUM.   7°00' W
TO O.P. DEP: 27 E
= D.LON: 42' E
∴ O.P. 50°22N. 6°18'W.

TO 24.0
026

AWAY
7.9

22.4
AWAY

50°N

257°
C.P. ARCT'S:

145°
C.P. ALTAIR.

C.P. MIRFAK.

1975　May 21st　Dawn sights in DR 50°10′N. 6°W.　I.E. −4′·0, HE 6 ft.

	ALPHERATZ	ALTAIR	ARCTURUS.
G.M.T	03 – 53 – 44	03 – 54 – 20	03 – 55 – 05
S.H.A.✳	358°13′·3　N 28°57′·2	62°35′·9　N 8°48′·1	146°21′·5　N 19°18′·5
G.H.A. ♈ 03^h	283°08·3	283°08·3	283°08·3
Incr:	13°28·2	13°37·2	13°48·5
	654°49·8	359°21·4	443°18·3
	−360°		−360°
G.H.A.✳	294°49·8	359°21·4	83°18·3
C.P. Long: W−	5°49·8	− 6°21·4	− 6°18·3
L.H.A.✳	289°	353°	77°
C.P. Lat:	N 50°	N 50°	N 50°
Dec:	N 28°57′	N 8°48′	N 19°18′
Hc	32°59′	47°36′	22°43′
d, + 41	+ 39	d+59　+ 47	d, +44　+ 13
TAB: ALT:	33°38′	48°23′	22°56′
			360°
			− 87
Z	84° = Zn.	107° = Zn	Z − 273° = Zn.
Sextant Alt:	33°41′·9	48°17′·3	22°53′·2
I.E. −4′·0			
Dip −2·4	−6·4	−6·4	−6·4
	33°35·5	48°10·9	22°46·8
Corn:	− 1·5	− 0·9	− 2·3
TRUE ALT:	33°34·0	48°10·0	22°44·5
TAB: "	33°38·0	48°23·0	22°56·0
Intercept:	AWAY 4·0	AWAY 13·0	AWAY 11·5
C.P.s	50°N. 5°49′·8 W	6°21′·4 W	6°18′·3 W.
Bearings	84°	107°	273°

11   1975 May 19th 15-54-12 GMT. DR. 49°50'N. 4°20'W. I.E. -2'0, HE 6 ft.

MOON.

GHA 15^h   298° 32'6 Dec: N 1° 36'4 H.P. 59'5
Incr: 54-12   12° 56.8   d, -13.0   - 11.8.
V. 10.2   9.4   N 1° 24'6
              311° 38.8

C.P. Long: W - 4° 38.8
    L.H.A.   307°
C.P. Lat: N 50°   Sextant Alt: Moon L.L.   23° 13'9
    Dec: N 1° 25'   I.E. - 2.0
                                    Dip - 2.4   - 4.4
                                              23° 09.5
    Hc   23° 35'   Conn: 61.4
d, + 50   + 21   H.P. 59.5   7.1
TAB: ALT: 23° 56   TRUE ALT: 24° 18.0
                              TAB: "   23° 56.0
    Z 119° = Zn.   Intercept: TO 22.0

OR. Using NP401, HO 229 or HD486:

    LHA   307°
    Lat: N 50°
    Dec: N 1° 24'6

    Hc   23° 35'3
d, 49.6   40 =   16.4   TRUE ALT: (as above) 24° 18'0
           9.6 =   3.9   TAB: "   23° 55.6
TAB: ALT: 23° 55'6   Intercept: TO 22.4

    Z 119°4 = Zn.

Using Marcq St Hilaire Haversine/Cosine Formula

1975   May 19th 15-54-12 GMT. DR.49°50'N. 4°20'W.   I.E.-2'·0, HE 6 ft.

   MOON.

GHA 15^h   298°32'·6 Dec: N 1°36'·4   H.P. 59'·5
    54-12   12° 56'·0 d-13·0   −11·8
  v. 10·2   9·3·   N 1° 24'·6
              311° 37·9
D.R. Long: W − 4° 20·0·
    LHA. 307° 17'·9 Log Hav 9·29450
DR. Lat: N 49° 50'·0 Log Cos 9·80957
   Dec: N 1° 24'·6 Log Cos 9·99987·
                     Log Hav 9·10394   Sextant Alt: MOON L.L. 23° 13'·9
                   = Nat: Hav ·12704   I.E. −2·0
Lat ~ Dec: 48°25'·4 →   "   "   ·16819   Dip −2·4   − 4·4
                      "   "   ·29523   23° 09·5
                                              Corr: 61·4
                   = C.Z.D. 65°49'·4   H.P. 59'·5   7·1
                     from 90°   TRUE ALT: 24° 18·0
               Calc: alt: 24°10'·6   CALC: "   24° 10·6
                                          Intercept: TO 7·4

Azimuth:

      TABLE A = S ·90
             B = N ·03
             C   S ·87 = S 60°·5E

             Bearing =   119°·5

12   1975 Feb 16ᵗʰ in DR. 43°S. 42°45'E.

Time of MOON's Mer: Pass:

Feb 16ᵗʰ   1551   LMT at 0°
ˣ Corr: for Long: 43°E   − 5
                             1546   LMT at DR

Long: in time, 42°45'E −2 51
    MER: PASS: 12 55   GMT at DR. ⊞

ˣ (Correction for Long:)
    Feb 16ᵗʰ   1551
         15ᵗʰ   1507 (E. long)
                    44ᵐ
    $\frac{43°}{360°} \times 44ᵐ = 5ᵐ$

(See also Naut: Almanac
  p xxxii Table Ⅱ, last
  buff page)

Sextant Alt: MOON L.L.   33° 25'.5 long N.
             I.E. − 2'.2
             Dip − 2.4   − 4.6
                             33° 20.9
          Corr: 57.4
     H.P. 54'.9   1.9
     TRUE ALT: 34° 20.2 N
          from 90°
        T.Z.D.   55° 39.8 S
Dec: 12ʰ 12°42'.6 N
d, +9.4 55ᵐ + 8.7   12° 51.3 N
        LAT: 42° 48'.5 S

⊞   Alternative method, to nearest second:

Reqᵈ LHA Moon   0° or 360°
    DR Long: E   − 42° 45'
    ∴ Reqᵈ GHA   317° 15'

Per Naut: Alm: 304° 05'.2 =   12ʰ
       remainder: 13° 09.8
       v. 13.8   12.5
                    12° 57.3 =   54ᵐ 17ˢ

TIME of Mer: Pass: at DR   12-54-17 GMT.

PROOF:
GHA 12ʰ   304° 05.2
     54-17   12° 57.2
  v 13.8   12.5
     GHA = 317° 14.9
DR Long: E+ 42° 45
            359° 59.9
                   .1
    LHA = $\begin{cases} 360° \\ \text{or } 0° \end{cases}$
on Merid: of the DR.

Plotting sheet No. 5333 A

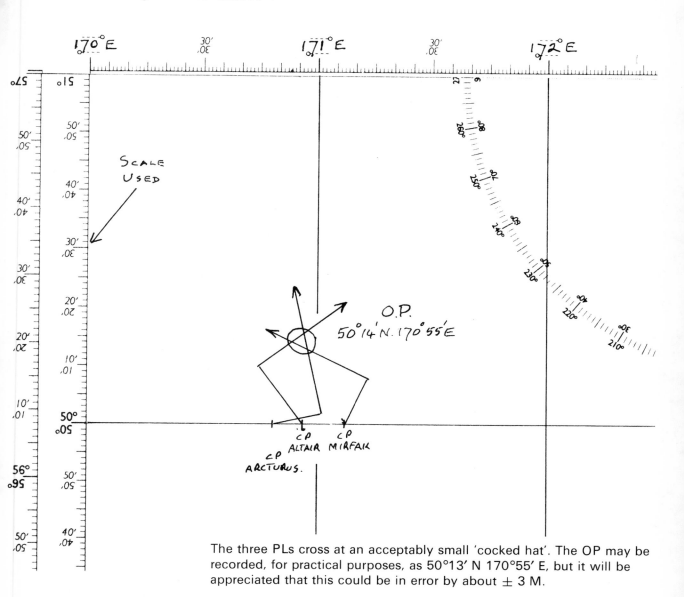

The three PLs cross at an acceptably small 'cocked hat'. The OP may be recorded, for practical purposes, as 50°13′ N 170°55′ E, but it will be appreciated that this could be in error by about ± 3 M.

14   1975 May 21st in DR. 49°45'N. 128°40'W.

Chron: 16-55-40 GMT.

Check for GD. Assume time   21^D 09.00 Rough LMT & Local date
DR Long: in time 128°40'W = + 8·35
∴ GD. 21^D 17·35 approx. GMT.

∴ use GD.21^D 16-55-40 GMT.

GHA Sun 21^{D}16^h 60°52'2 Dec: N 20°08'9
      55-40   13°56·0 d+0·5   +0·5
             74°48'2   N 20°09'4
             360
            434°48·2
D.R. Long: W-128° 40   use for AP 3270.
   LHA.   306° 08·2   306° ⎫
DR. Lat: N 49°45   N 50° ⎬ = Z 105° = Zn.
   Dec: N 20° 09·4   N 20° ⎭

<u>Sun's Bearing.</u> by steering compass   074° C
                by Sun's Azimuth   105° T
                TOTAL ERROR   31° E

   Variation   24° E
∴ Deviation   7° E. (on yacht's heading at the time)
   Total Error 31° E.

15   1975 Aug 29ᵗʰ Dawn sights in DR 36°10'N. 71°20'W   IE −1'6, HE 8 ft.

	POLARIS	RIGEL	SIRIUS	JUPITER.
GMT	09-52-13	09-52-48	09-53-10	09-53-57

GHA ♈ 111° 57'.0   111° 57'.0   111° 57.0   JUPITER 88° 50'.0 Dec N8°01'.6
　　　　　13° 05.4　　　13° 14.2　　　13° 19.7　　　　　　　13° 29.3 d −1 − 0.1
　　　　　――――――　SHA 281° 39.4 .58 13.6 SHA 258° 58.9. S16° 40.8　v 2.6　　2.3　　N8°01.5
　　　　　125° 02.4　　406° 50.6　　　384° 15.6　　　　　102° 21.6
D.R. Long W −71° 20.0 CP −70° 50.6　　− 71° 15.6　　　 −71° 21.6.
　LHA ♈ 53° 42'.4　　✶ 336°　　　　✶ 313°　　　Jupiter 31°
　　　　　C.P. Lat: N36°　　　　N 36°　　　　　　N36°
　　　　　　Dec: S 8°14'　　　S 16° 41'　　　　　N 8°01'

　　　　　Hc　40°33'　　　　21°37'　　　　　50°13'
　　　d, −54　　−13　　−46　−31　　　+46　　+ 1
　TAB: ALT: 40° 20'　　　　21° 06'　　　　50° 14
　　　　　　　　　　　　　　　　　　　　360°
　　　Z　148° = Zn　　Z 131° = Zn.　　Z −127°
　　　　　　　　　　　　　　　　　　　　233° = Zn

Sext. Alt.　　36°45'.0　　40°29'.5　　21°30'.0　　50°09'.0
　IE −1'6
　Dip −2.7　　−4.3　　　−4.3　　　−4.3　　　−4.3
　　　　　36° 40.7　　40° 25.2　　21° 25.7　　50° 04.7
　Corn:　　−1.3　　　−1.1　　　−2.5　　　−0.8
　　　　　36° 39.4　TRUE 40° 24.1　21° 23.2　　50° 03.9
　A₀　　11.6　TAB: 40° 20.0　21° 06.0　　50° 14.0
　A₁　　　.6　Int'cpt: TO 4.1　TO 17.2　　AWAY 10.1
　A₂　　　.3
　　　　36° 51.9
　　　　− 1°
　LAT: 35° 51'.9

O. P. 35° 52' N. 70° 56' W.

Plotting sheet No. 5333 A

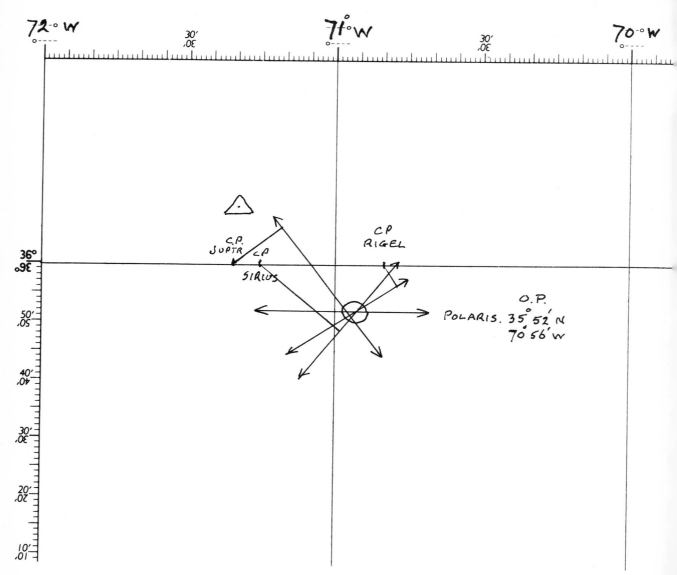

15.a   *Using Marcq St Hilaire Haversine/Cosine Formula*

Aug 29th DR 36°10'N. 71°20'W.   I.E. −1.6 HE 8 ft.

	RIGEL.	SIRIUS	JUPITER.
at G.M.T.	09-52-48	09-53-10	09-53-57.

	RIGEL	SIRIUS	JUPITER
SHA ✱	281°39'.4 S8°13'.6	258°58'.9 S16°40'.8	GHA Jupiter. 88°50'.0 N8°01'.6
GHA ♈	111° 57.0	111° 57.0	13°29.3. d −1 −0.1
Incr :	13° 14.2	13° 19.7	v. 2.6 2.3. N8°01'.5
			102° 21.6
GHA.	406° 50.6	384° 15.6	
D.R. Long: W −	71° 20.	− 71° 20.	− 71° 20.
L.H.A.	335° 30'.6 H8.65305	312° 55'.6 9.20268	31° 01.6 8.85453.
DR. Lat: N	36° 10' cq.90704	N 36° 10'. 9.90704	N 36° 10'. 9.90704
Dec: S	8° 13'.6 cq.99551	S 16° 40'.8 9.98133	N 8° 01'.5 9.99573.
	H.8.55560	9.09105	8.75730.
	= .03594	.12332	.05719.
Lat: ~ Dec: 44°23'.6	.14272	52° 50'.8 .19802	28°08.5 .05910.
	.17866	.32134	.11629.
C.Z.D.	50°00'.5	69°03'.8	39°52'.6
from	90°	90°	90°
CALC: ALT:	39° 59'.5	20° 56.2	50° 07.4.
Sextant Alt:	40° 29'.5	21° 30'.0	50° 09'.0.
IE −1.6			
Dip −2.7.	−4.3	−4.3	−4.3.
	40° 25.2	21° 25.7	50° 04.7.
Corn:	−1.1	− 2.5	− 0.8.
TRUE ALT:	40° 24.1	21° 23.2	50° 03.9.
CALC: "	39° 59.5	20° 56.2.	50° 07.4
Intercept:	TO 24.6	TO 27.0	AWAY 3.5

TABLE A =	S 1.60	S .68	S 1.21
B =	S .35.	S .41	N .27
C	S 1.95 = S 32°.2 E	S 1.09 = S 48°.6 E	S .94 = S 52°.7 W.
	= 147°.8	= 131°.4	= 232°.7

O.P. 35°52'N. 70°56'W.

Plotting sheet No. 5333 A

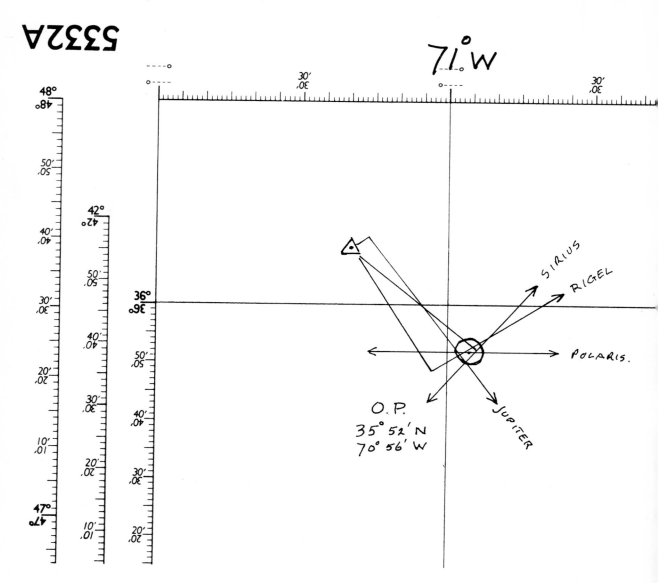

15.b

O.P. Aug 29 dawn $35°52'N. 70°56'W$

RUN: $115°T$ $12.5M.$ Current: $040°$ at $2kn × 2^h = 4M.$

D.R. at Aug 29th 11.52 $35°50'N. 70°39'W$ (see plot.)

1975 Aug 29th at $11-52-09$ GMT   Sun observed, IE -1.6. Ht.E. 8 ft.

$$GHA\ 11^h\ 344°\ 43.9 \quad Dec: N\ 9°29'.9$$
$$52-09 \quad \underline{13°\ 02.3} \quad d-0.9 \quad \underline{-0.8.}$$
$$357°\ 46.2 \quad N\ 9°\ 29.1$$

C.P. Long: $W-70°\ 46.2.$
L.H.A. $287°$
C.P. Lat: $N\ 36°$
Dec: $N\ 9°29'$

Hc $19°00'$
d$+34$ $\underline{+16}$
TAB: ALT: $\underline{19°16'}$

Sextant Alt: LL. $19°16.0$
$\quad$ IE -1.6
$\quad$ Dip -2.7 $\underline{-4.3}$
$\qquad\qquad 19°\ 11.7$
Conn: $\underline{+13.3}$
TRUE ALT: $19°25.0$
TAB: ALT: $\underline{19°16.0}$
Intercept: $\quad$ TO $\quad 9.0$

Z $\underline{93°} = Zn.$

c

RUN: $125°$ $27M$ Current: $040°$ at $1kn × 4^h = 4M.$

Aug 29th Mer: Pass: 1201
DR Long: $70°W + \underline{440}$
$\qquad\qquad\qquad 1641$ GMT at DR.

Sextant Alt: L.L. $63°33.7$ S
IE & Dip $\quad \underline{-4.3}$
$\qquad\qquad 63°\ 29.4$
Conn: $\quad \underline{+15.5.}$
TRUE ALT: $63°\ 44.9$ S
from $\quad \underline{90°}$
TZD $\quad 26°\ 15.1$ N.
Dec: 16^h $9°25.5N.$
d, -0.9 41^m $\underline{-0.6}$ $9°24.9$ N.
$\underline{LAT\ 35°40'.0\ N}$

$\underline{O.P.\ 35°40'N.\ 70°05'W.}$ $\qquad$ Per Plot.

Plotting sheet No. 5333 A

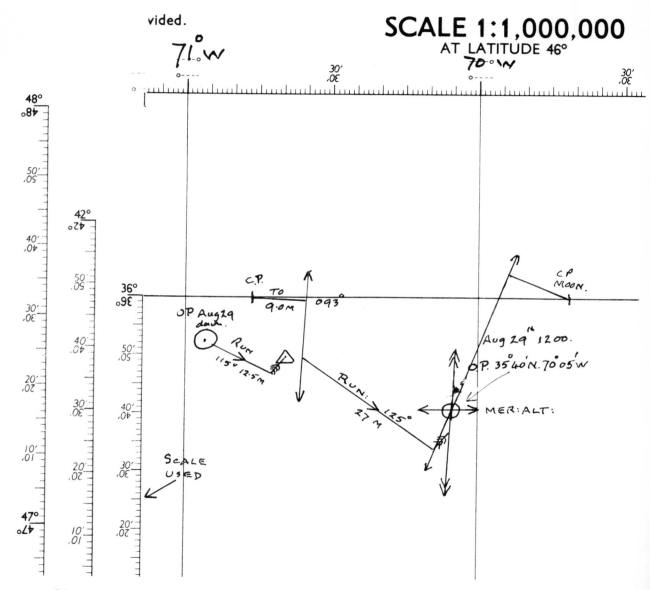

d

Aug 29th 16-52-21 GMT.   DR 35°N 70°05'W.   I.E. -1·6, HE 8 ft.

   MOON.

GHA 16h   157°03·2. Dec: N 20°00·0.
   52-21   12°29·5   d+3·5   + 3·1
   v. 10·2   8·9   N20°03·1
            169°41·6.
CP Long: W- 69°41·6   Sextant Alt: MOON. L.L.   3°17·1
   LHA 100°   IE -1·6
CP Lat: N 36°   Dip -2·7.   -4·3
   Dec: N 20°03'   3°12·8

                                          Corn: 54·4
   Hc 3°57'   H.P. 55·9   2·7.
   d, +37   + 2.   TRUE ALT: 4°09·9
TAB: ALT: 3°59'.   TAB: ALT: 3°59·0.
                  360°   Intercept: TO   10·9.
         Z - 68°
            292° = Zn.   O.P. 35°40'N. 70°04'W.

e

   RUN: 125°T 28M.   Current: 040° 1 kn × 4h = 4M.

Aug 29th 20-53-18 GMT.   DR. 35°28'N. 69°33'W   IE -1·6, H.E. 8 ft.

GHA 20h   119°45·6   Dec: N 9°21·9
   53-18   13°19·5   d-0·9   -0·8.
            133°05·1   N 9°21·1
CP. Long: W- 70°05·1
   LHA   63°   Sextant Alt: L.L.   26°41·8
CP. Lat: N 35°   I.E. -1·6
   Dec: N 9°21'   Dip -2·7   -4·3
                                                 26°37·5
   Hc 27°12'   Corn: + 14·1
   d. +34   + 12.   TRUE ALT: 26°51·6
TAB: ALT: 27°24'.   TAB: ALT: 27°24·0.
                  360°   Intercept: AWAY 32·4.
         Z - 98°
            262° = Zn.

Plotting sheet No. 5333 A

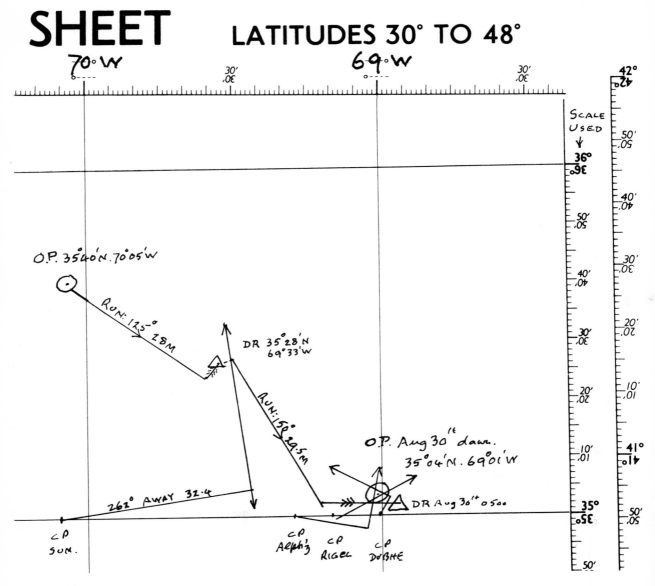

SHEET LATITUDES 30° TO 48°
70° W   69° W

O.P. 35°40'N. 70°05'W

RUN: 125-° 28M

DR 35°28'N 69°33'W

RUN: 158°-29.5M

O.P. Aug 30th dawn.
35°04'N. 69°01'W

DR Aug 30th 0500

262° AWAY 32.4

CP SUN.

CP Alpha'g

CP RIGEL

CP DUBHE

SCALE USED

36°

35°

41°

42°

88

f

Aug 30th.　　　c. Twilight will be - N 35° 0505 LMT.

　　　　　　DR Long in time, 70°W　　+ 4 40

　　　　　　　　　　　　　0945 GMT at DR.

Sight taken Aug 29th at 20-53 GMT.

Time elapsed, approx. 13 hrs.

RUN to 30th 0945 GMT. 29·5 M Co. 150°T. Current 090° 1kn = Drift, 13 M

Advance Plan. say at 09-52-00 GMT. DR. 35°03'N 68°56'W.

GHA ♈ 09^h　112° 56·2

　　52^m　13° 02·1.

　　　　　125° 58·3

DR. Long: W-69° 43

LHA ♈ 56° 15' — use 56°

Per AP3270 Vol: 1

	Alt.	Zn.
Dubhe	22°08'	029°
RIGEL	41°54'	150°
Alpheratz	44°10'	278°

Observations :

	Dubhe	RIGEL	Alpheratz.
at GMT	09-52-07	09-52-49	09-53-18.
GHA ♈ 09^h	112° 56·2	112° 56·2	112° 56·2
52-07	13° 03·9	52-49 13° 14·4	53-18 13 21·7
	126° 00·1	126° 10·6	126° 17·9
C.P. Long: W—	69° 00·1	— 69° 10·6	— 69° 17·9
LHA ♈	57°	57°	57°
C.P. Lat:	N 35°	N 35°	N 35°
Hc	22° 32'	Hc 42° 18'	Hc 43° 21'
Zn	029°	Zn 151°	Zn 279°
Sextant Alt: ✱	22° 42·2	42° 24·2	43° 13·8
IE −1·6			
Dip −2·7	−4·3.	−4·3	−4·3.
	22° 37·9	42° 19·9	43° 09·5.
Corr:	−2·3	−1·1	−1·0.
TRUE ALT:	22° 35·6	42° 18·8	43° 08·5
TAB: ALT:	22° 32·0	42° 18·0	43° 21·0.
Intercept :	TO 3·6	TO 0·8	AWAY 12·5

O.P. 35°04'N. 69°01'W.

16   33° S. 72° W   to   41° S. 175° E

<u>Great Circle Track.</u>

NORIE'S TABLES
p.

		72° W			
		185° W			
D. Long:		113°	log Hav	9.84 221.	491
Lat:	S 33°		log Cos	9.92 359.	226
Lat:	S 41°		log Cos	<u>9.87778.</u>	234.
			log Hav:	9.64358	
			= nat: Hav:	.44013	480
Lat ~ Lat.	8° →		nat: Hav:	<u>.00487</u>	405
			nat: Hav	.44500	
					480.

∠ Z D = 83° 41'.2 = <u>5,021.2 M</u>

<u>Rhumbline</u>

	Meridional Parts	
Lat. 33°	2,086.78	142
Lat. 41°	2,686.24	144.
D.M.P.	599.46	

Long: 72° W

„ 175° E = 185° W

D. Long.	113° × 60 =	6,780' = log	3.83123	168
D. M.P.		599.46 = log	<u>2.77775.</u>	167
		log tan:	1.05348	
		↓		} 277
	33°	= log sec:	1.05532	
	41°			
D. Lat.	8° × 60 =	480' = log	<u>2.68124</u>	165
		log	3.73656	
		=	<u>5,452 M.</u>	166.

Gt. Circle Track less than Rhumbline by 431 M.

17   Check for perpendicularity
              side error
              index error.
If any adjustment is made, re-check all again in the same sequence,
since any one adjustment may affect the other two errors. (Unless index
error is excessive, do not adjust mirror.)

Answers 3

1 1975 May 19th in DR 15° 10' N. 59° 15' W   I E +2'.0. Ht E 8 ft.

Mer: Pass: 11 56   L M T.
DR. Long: in time 59° 15' W +3 57.
_____
                          15 53   GMT at DR.

Sextant A lt: L.L.   84° 59'.7 N.
                    IE +2'0
                    Dip -2.7   -0.7.
                    _____
                                84° 59.0
                    Conn: +15.8.
              TRUE ALT: 85° 14.8   N
                    from   90°
                    _____
                    T.Z.D.   4° 45'.2   S
         DEC: 15^h 19° 43'.2 N.
      d, +0.5   53^m +0.4 19° 43.6   N.
                    _____
              L AT: 14° 58'.4 N.
              =========================

Note :   Due to the extremely high altitude, this would be a difficult
         sight to take and would be unreliable. In these circumstances
         it would be better to take multiple star sights at dawn and/or
         dusk twilight.

2

1975   Feb 17th 09-52-05 GMT.   DR 50°15'N. 6°50'W.   IE −1.9, HE 8 ft.

G.H.A 09^h 311° 28.6   S 12° 08.7
52-05   13° 01.3. d,-0.9   −0.8.
         324° 29.9   S 12° 07.9.
C.P. Long: W − 6° 29.9.
   L.H.A   318°
C.P. Lat: N 50°
   Dec: S 12° 07.9.

        Hc   17° 56'
d, −53   − 7.
TAB: ALT: 17° 49'

     Z   137° = Zn.

Sextant Alt: L.L. 17° 27.0
   IE −1.9
   Dip −2.7.   −4.6
              17° 22.4
   Corr: + 13.2.
TRUE ALT: 17° 35.6
   TAB: .   17° 49.0.
Intercept: AWAY 13.4.

4

Moonrise   Aug 30th in   32° N. 54° W.

Aug 30th . 30° N. 30^D 23-49^s.
   Cor: y^n lat: 2°   − 4.   a)
            32° N.   23 - 45.
   Cor: y^n long: 54°W   + 15   b)
                24 00   LMT.
Long: in time, 54°   + 3 36
         GD. 31^D 03 36   GMT.

a) Cor: y^n lat:
   30° N.   23 49
   35° N.   23 37.
   5°   − 12.
   2° =   − 4^m

b.) Cor: y^n long:
           30°
   30^D 23-49
   31^D 24-45
1 day = 360° = + 56^m
∴ 54° = 56^m × $\frac{54°}{360°}$ = 15^m

92

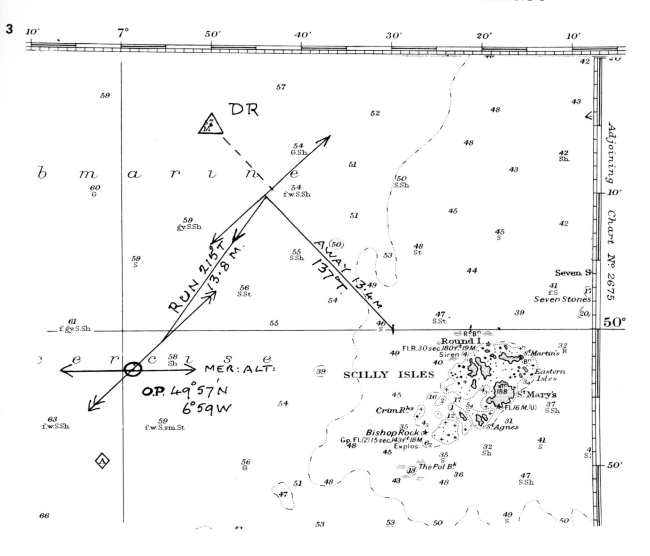

3

10' 7° 50' 40' 30' 20' 10'

Adjoining Chart No. 2675

59

57

DR

52

48

43

42

marine

54
G.Sh

51

48

50
S.Sh

42
Sh

60
G

54
f.w.S.Sh

45

43

10'

59
gy.S.Sh

51

45

42

45
S

59
S

55
S.Sh

AWAY 137°T. 13.4 M.

53

48
St

44

Seven S

RUN 215° 13.8 M.

(50)

49

41
f.S
Seven Stones

17

56
S.St

54

20

61
f.gy.S.Sh

55

46
S

47
S.St

39

50°

49

R Bn
Round I.
Fl.R.30sec.180ft 19M.
Siren (4)

32
R

erc e
58
Sh
i s e
MER: ALT:

40

St Martin's
B

Eastern
Isles

(39)

SCILLY ISLES

34

O.P. 49°57'N
6°59W

54

45

16

17

R
158

St Mary's

37
S.Sh

63
f.w.S.Sh

59
f.w.S.sm St

Crim.Rks

1

12

Fl./6 M.(U)

31

St Agnes

41
S

A

35

Bishop Rock
Gp.Fl.(2)15sec.143ft 18M.
48   Explos.

6

45

32
Sh

4
S

50'

56
G

35
S

13

The Pol Bk

36

47
S.Sh

66

51

48

43

48

49
S

50

47

53

53

50

5

1975 Feb. 16ᵗʰ in DR 35°S. 105°E. Dawn.

$$\begin{array}{ll}
\text{Zone Time (by ship's clock)} & 16^D\ 05\ 05 \\
\text{apply } \mathbf{Z} & \underline{\quad -7\quad} \\
\text{GD} & 15^D\ 22\text{-}05 \quad \text{approx GMT.}
\end{array}$$

$$\begin{array}{lr}
\text{chron: shows} \quad 10\text{-}07\text{-}34.\ \text{Read as} & 22\text{-}07\text{-}34 \\
\text{D.W.E. Slow} + & \underline{\quad 2\text{-}18.} \\
\text{Use for sight}\ \ \text{G.D.15}^D & \underline{\underline{22\text{-}09\text{-}52\ \ \text{GMT.}}}
\end{array}$$

6.a

June 10ᵗʰ   DR. 47°N. 179°30'E.

$$\begin{array}{lll}
\text{Evening Twilight} & \text{about} & 10^D\ 20\text{-}30^{m\ \ s}\ \text{Local time} \\
\text{DR. Long: in time} & E- & \underline{\quad 11\text{-}58.} \\
& & 10^D\ 08\text{-}32 \quad \text{approx: GMT.}
\end{array}$$

$$\text{Time by chron:} \qquad 8\text{-}21\text{-}15$$

$$\text{Use} \quad \text{GD. }10^D.\ \underline{\underline{08\text{-}21\text{-}15\ \text{GMT.}}}$$

b

Log Book will show (for example) :

$$\begin{array}{ll}
& Z-12. \\
\text{June 10}^{ᵗʰ} & \underline{23\ 30.} \\
& Z+12 \\
10^{ᵗʰ} & 00\ 30.
\end{array}$$

$$\begin{array}{lll}
\text{A.M. Civil Twilight. Lat: 47°N. about} & 10^D\ 0330 & \text{LMT.} \\
& Z \quad +12 & \\
& \text{GD. }10^D\ \ 1530 & \text{approx GMT.}
\end{array}$$

$$\text{Use: GD. }10^D.\ \underline{\underline{15\text{-}08\text{-}45\ \text{GMT.}}}$$

7   1975 May 21st a.m. Twilight in DR 50°N. 170°E.

$$\begin{array}{ll}
\text{C. Twilight} & 21^D \; 03 \; 28 \;\; LMT. \\
\text{Long: in time, 170°E} & \underline{\;\; - \; 11 \;\; 20} \\
& GD \; 20^D \;\; 16 \;\; 08 \;\; \text{approx GMT.}
\end{array}$$

$$\underline{\text{Use} \;\; GD \; 20^D \;\; 15\text{-}54\text{-}45 \;\; GMT.}$$

$$\begin{array}{lll}
GHA \; \Upsilon \;\; 20^D \, 15^h & 102° \, 38.8 \\
\quad\quad\quad 54\text{-}45 & \underline{\; 13° \;\; 43.5} \\
& 116° \;\; 22.3 \\
DR. Long: \; E+ & \underline{170°} \\
\underline{\underline{L \, HA \; \Upsilon}} & \underline{\underline{286° \;\; 22.3}}
\end{array}$$

$$\begin{array}{llr}
\underline{\text{Sextant Alt:}} \; POLARIS & 49° \; 40.2 \\
\quad\quad\quad IE. \, - 4.2 \\
\quad\quad\quad Dip \, \underline{- 2.4} & \underline{- 6.6} \\
& 49° \; 33.6 \\
\quad\quad\quad Corr: & \underline{- 0.8} \\
& 49° \; 32.8 \\
\quad\quad\quad A_o & 1° \; 13.0 \\
\quad\quad\quad A_1 & .6 \\
\quad\quad\quad A_2 & \underline{\quad .3} \\
& 50° \; 46.7 \\
& \underline{- 1°} \\
\underline{\underline{LAT:}} & \underline{\underline{49° 46.7}}
\end{array}$$

Answers 3

8

1975 Feb 16ᵗʰ at 01-55-33 GMT. DR 50°15′S. 92°W. I.E. +3′·0. Ht.E 6 ft.

p.m. Twilight   50°S   16ᴰ 19-55   approx LMT.
DR Long: in time 92°W   +   6 08.
                G.D. 17ᴰ 02-03   approx GMT.

GHA 17ᴰ 01ʰ   57° 48·5   Dec: N 22°32′·8
     55-33ˢ   13° 53·3.   d 00.
  v. 2·6   2·4.
             71° 44·2
             360°
           431° 44·2

CP. Long: W − 91° 44·2   **Sextant Alt:** SATURN   15° 12′·7
   L.H.A.   340°   I.E +3·0
CP. Lat: S   50°   Dip − 2·4
   Dec: N   22° 33′   + 0·6.
                                   15° 13·3

          Hc   15° 51′   Corn: − 3·5.
  d, − 59   − 32.   TRUE ALT: 15° 09·8.
  TAB: ALT: 15° 19′   TAB: "   15° 19·0.
                     Intercept: AWAY   9·2

            180°
       Z − 161°
          019° = Zn.

9   1975 May 20th DR. 50°20'N. 173°45'E.

Advance Plan:

   a.m. C. Twilight 50°N. 20^D 03-28 L.M.T.
   DR. Long: in time 173°45 E —   11-35
                              GD. 19^D 15-53 approx G.M.T.

G.H.A. ♈ 19^{D}15^h 101°39'.6
        52^{m}00   13° 02.1
                       114° 41.7
   DR Long: E + 173° 45
   L.H.A ♈   288° 26'.7

      use LHA 288°

{ Mirfak   21°10'   036°
  ALTAIR   48°04'   166°
  ARCTURUS 24°38'   271°

Sights taken: Mirfak   ALTAIR   ARCTURUS
   at GD 19^D. GMT 15-52-56   15-53-35   15-54-10.

G.H.A. ♈ 19^{D}15^h 101° 39'.6   101° 39'.6   101° 39'.6
        52-56 13° 16.2   53-35 13° 26.0   54-10 13° 34.7
               114° 55.8   115° 05.6   115° 14.3
   C.P. Long: E+174° 04.2   173° 54.4   173° 45.7
        L.H.A. 289°   289°   289°
   C.P. Lat: N 50°   N 50°   N 50°

        Hc 21°32'   Hc 48°13'   Hc 23°59'

        Zm 036°   168°   272°

Sextant Alt: ✱   21°47'.8   48° 08'.0   24° 02'.5
            I.E. −3.4
            Dip −3.1   −6.5   −6.5   −6.5
                      21° 41.3   48° 01.5   23° 56.0
        Corn: − 2.4   − 0.9   − 2.2
        TRUE ALT: 21° 38.9   48° 00.6   23° 53.8
        TAB: "   21° 32.0   48° 13.0   23° 59.0.
   Intercept: TO   6.9   AWAY 12.4   AWAY 5.2.

        O.P. 50° 14'N. 174° 03'E.

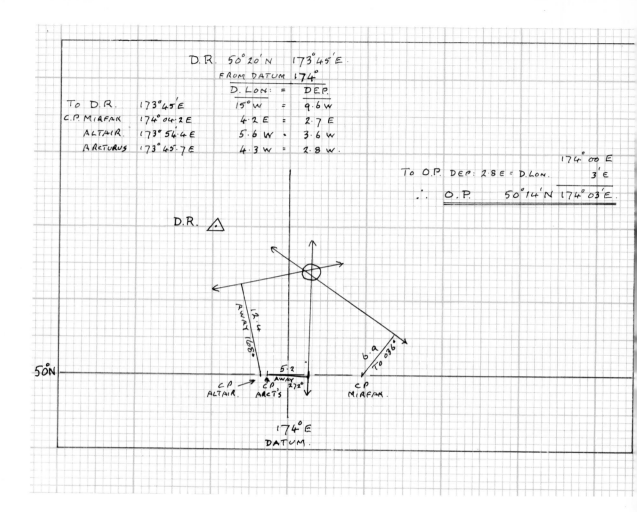

D.R. 50°20'N 173°45'E.

FROM DATUM 174°

		D. LON.	=	DEP.
TO D.R.	173°45'E	15°W	=	9·6 W
C.P. MIRFAK	174°04·2E	4·2 E	=	2·7 E
ALTAIR	173°54·4E	5·6 W	=	3·6 W
ARCTURUS	173°45·7E	4·3 W	=	2·8 W.

174° 00 E

TO O.P. DEP: 2·8E = D.LON.   3'E

∴   O.P.   50°14'N 174°03'E.

D.R. △

12·4
AWAY 168°

6·9
TO 036°

5·2
AWAY 272°

50°N

C P → ALTAIR.   C.P ARCT'S.

C P MIRFAK.

174°E
DATUM.

10

1975 Feb 16th in DR. 50°15'S 92°W.   I.E. +3·0, HE 6 ft.

p.m. C.Twilight 16D 1955 approx LMT.
DR Long: in time 92°W +   6 08
GD 17D 02·03. approx GMT.

BETELGEUSE.
at   GD 17D. GMT 01-52-47.

SHA *   271° 32'·2 Dec: N 7°24'·1
GHA ♈ 17D 01h 161° 23·5
       52-47s   13° 13·9
GHA *   446° 09·6
C.P. Long: W— 92° 09·6
    LHA * 354°
C.P. Lat: S 50°   Sextant Alt: 32° 19'·8
     Dec: N 7° 24'   IE +3·0
                                 Dip −2·4   +0·6
                                            32° 20·4
    Hc   32° 46'   Corn: − 1·5·
d, −60   −24.   TRUE ALT: 32° 18·9
TAB: ALT: 32° 22'   TAB: "   32° 22·0
                            Intercept: AWAY 3·1
         180°
   Z   −173°
         007° = Zn.

SEE PLOT for ANS: N° 11.

1.   See Ocean Yacht Navigator Chapter 3, p 27.

11

1975 Feb 16th at 01-52-12 GMT. DR. 50°15'S. 92°W. IE +3'·0, HE 6 ft.

<u>MOON</u>. (For GD calc: see Q 10)

GHA. 17^D 01^h 133° 07'·1 <u>Dec</u>: N. 14° 39'·9   <u>H.P. 55'·2</u>
     52-12   12° 27·3. d, +8·7   + 7·6
     V. 13·0   <u>   11·4</u>   N. 14° 47·5
             145° 45·8

C.P. Long: W – <u>91° 45·8</u>
   LHA   54°

C.P. Lat: S 50°
   Dec: N 14° 47'   <u>Sextant Alt</u>: MOON L.L. 8° 53'·0
                               IE +3·0
                            Dip <u>–2·4</u> <u>+ 0·6</u>
      H$_c$ 10° 27'   8° 53·6
  d, –51   <u>– 40.</u>   <u>Corn</u>:   61·6
<u>TAB: ALT: 9° 47</u>   <u>H.P. 55'·2</u>   <u>1·8.</u>
                          TRUE ALT: 9° 57·0
        180°   TAB: "   <u>9° 47·0.</u>
   Z + <u>127</u>   <u>Intercept</u>:   TO 10·0.
        307° = **Z**n

<u>O.P.   50° 03'S 92° 08'W.</u>   See Plot.

Plotting sheet No. 5333 A

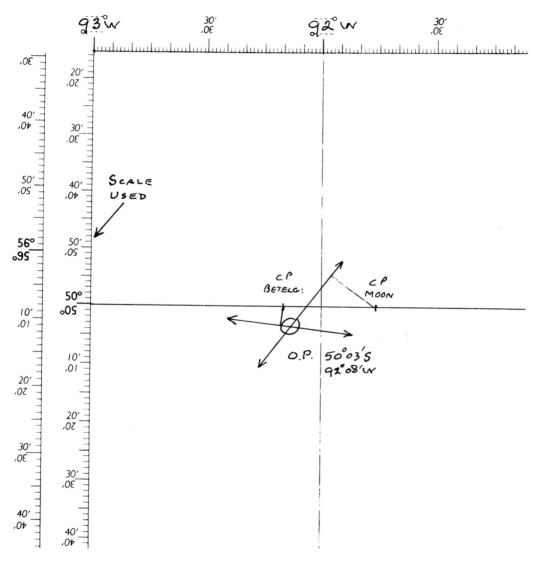

12

1975 May 20th in DR 52°20'N 40°W.

TIME OF MOON MER: PASS:

MOON MER: PASS: 20 06
⊗ Corr: for Long: 40°W + 6
                       20 12
   DR Long: in time, 40°W. + 2 40.
   G.M.T. at DR   22 52   *

⊗ May 20^D 2006
        21^D 20 58.
1 day, = 360° =   + 52^m
∴ 40° = 52^m × $\frac{40°}{360°}$ = 5.8^m

Sextant Alt: MOON L.L. 31° 13.7 S
             IE − 3.2
             Dip − 2.7.   − 5.9
                        31° 07.8
        Corr: 58.5
        H.P. 59.5   7.0.
   TRUE ALT: 32° 13.3 S
       from   90°
            57° 46.7 N
DEC: 22^h 5° 04.25
d, +12.7, 52^m + 11.1   5° 15.3 S
       LAT: 52° 31.4 N

* A**lternative** method, to nearest second:

Req^d Moon L.H.A. 0°
   DR Long: W   40°
   G.H.A req^d 40°.

            27°34.9 = 22^h
   v. 9.9   8.5.
            27° 43.4
   remainder 12° 16.6 = 51^m 27^s

TIME: 22 − 51 − 27 GMT.

PROOF:
G.H.A 22^h 27° 34.9
Incr: 51.27. 12° 16.6
   v. 9.9   8.5.
   G.H.A.   40° 00.0
DR Long: W −40°
   L.H.A.   0°
   on on DR's Merid:

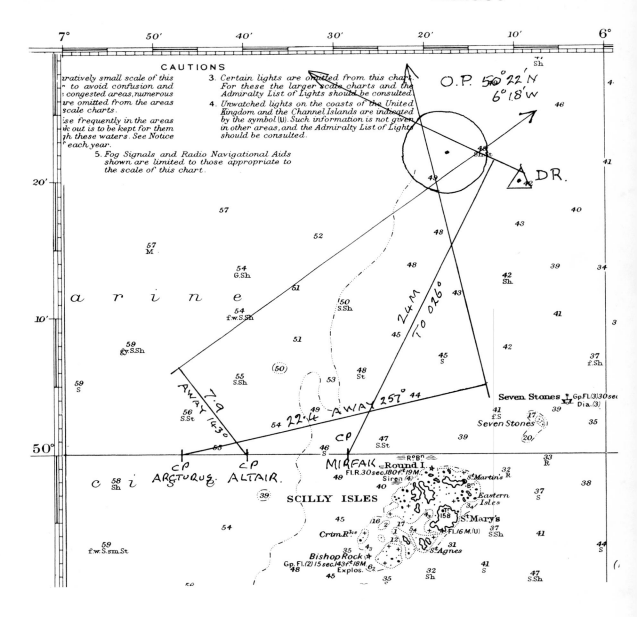

14

Compass check – 1975 Aug 29th 11-52-09 GMT. DR 49°50'N 70°40'W

$$GHA \quad 11^h \quad 344° 43'·9 \quad \underline{Dec: N 9° 29'·9}$$
$$52-09 \quad \underline{13° 02·3} \quad d.-0·9 \quad -0·8.$$
$$357° 46·2 \quad \underline{N 9° 29·1}$$

DR. Long: W – 70° 40
LHA. 287° 06·2
DR Lat: N 49° 50
Dec: N 9° 29·1

$$use \begin{cases} 287° \\ N 50° \\ N 9° \end{cases}$$

$$Z = \underline{97°} = Zn$$

Compass Bearing taken of sun 111° C

$$Var: \underline{-21°}$$
$$090° M.$$

Azimuth $\underline{097° T}$

∴ Deviation $\underline{7°E}$

111° C
97° T
TOTAL ERROR 14° W.   on ship's heading at the time.

OR, Using ABC Tables:

LHA 287° 06'
Lat: N 49° 50'
Dec: N 9° 29'

$$A = S ·36$$
$$B = \underline{N ·17}$$
$$C, \quad S ·19 = S 83° E$$
$$= \underline{097° T}$$

15.a 1975 May 19th dawn, DR 50°10'N. 129°30'W. IE −1.9, HE 6 ft.

check for GD.   C. Twilight 19^D 03-28 LMT approx.
        DR Long: in time, 129°30'W + 8-38
                              GD 19^D 12-06 approx GMT.

<u>Sights taken:</u>   <u>POLARIS</u>   <u>ARCTURUS</u>
       at   GMT   11-53-05   11-53-51.

                                    SHA ✳ 146° 21·5 N 19° 18·5
       GHA ♈ 11^h   41° 29·8   GHA ♈   41° 29·8
           53-05   13° 18·4   53-51   13° 30·0·
                      54° 48·2   GHA ✳ 201° 21·3.
                      360
                      414° 48·2.

       DR. Long: W−129° 30   CP Long: W−129° 21·3.
        LHA ♈ 285° 18·2.   LHA ✳   72°
                              CP. Lat: N 50°
                                Dec: N 19° 18'

                                Itc   25° 56'
                              d, + 43   + 13.
                              TAB: ALT: 26° 09'
                                       360°
                              Z. − 91
                                   269° = Zn.

   <u>Sextant Alt.</u>   50° 05'·0   26° 28'·9
       IE −1·9
       Dip −2·4   − 4·3   − 4·3·
                    50° 00·7   26° 24·6
       Conn: − 0·8   − 1·9.
    TRUE ALT 49° 59·9   TRUE ALT 26° 22·7
       A₀   1° 14·1   TAB: " 26° 09·0·
       A₁   ·6   <u>Intercept_ TO 13·7</u>
       A₂   ·3
               51° 14·9
               −1°
    LAT: 50° 14·9

        <u>O.P. 50° 15'N. 129° 43'W.</u>

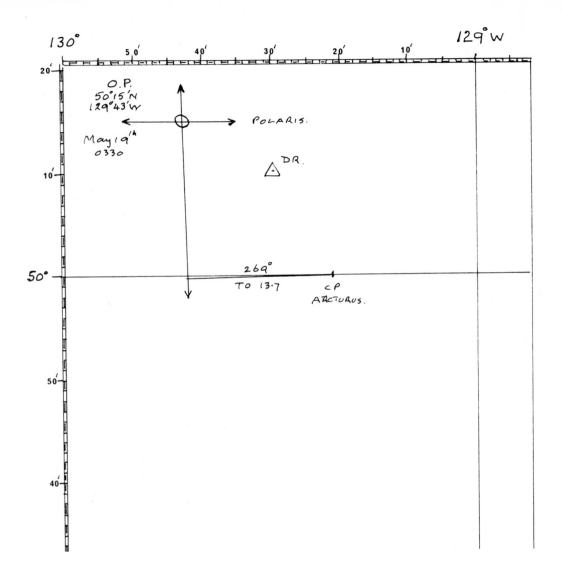

130°   129° W

50'   40'   30'   20'   10'

20'

O.P.
50°15' N
129°43' W

POLARIS.

May 19ᵗʰ
0330

△ DR.

10'

50°

269°

TO 13·7   C P
ARCTURUS.

50'

40'

b

RUN: 115°T. Distance 68 M.

May 19ᵗ DR. 49°47'N. 128°07'W

check yr G.D. — say 19ᴰ 1600 LMT.
DR long: in time, 128°W = + 8 3 2
  G.D. 20ᴰ 0032 GMT approx.

Sights taken:

	SUN	MOON
at GMT 20ᴰ	00-55-09	00-55-47.

SUN	MOON
G H A .00ʰ 180°53.6 N 19°48.1	68°55.6 S 0°20.4 H.P. 59.5
55-09. 13° 47.3 d+0.5 +0.5	13° 18.6 d+13.0 +12.0
N 19°48.6	V.10.2 9.4 S 0°32.4
194° 40.9	82° 23.6
	+ 360
	442° 23.6.
C.P. Long: W-127° 40.9	− 128° 23.6.
L H A 67°	314°
C.P. Lat: N 50°	N 50°
Dec: N 19° 49'	S 0° 32'

He 29°08'	360°	He 26°31'	
d, +44 + 36	Z − 95	d −51 − 27.	Z 127°= Zn.
TAB: ALT: 29°44'	265°= Zn.	TAB: ALT: 26°04'	

Sextant Alt: L.L. 29°46.2   L.L. 25°26.5
  I E −1.9
  Dip −2.4. − 4.3   − 4.3.
    29°41.9   25°22.2
  Corr: + 14.3   Corr: 60.7
         H.P. 59.5   7.0.
             26°29.9
    TRUE ALT: 29°56.2.   26° 04.0.
    TAB: " 29°44.0
  Intercept: TO 12.2   TO 25.9.

O.P. 49°39'N. 127°58'W.

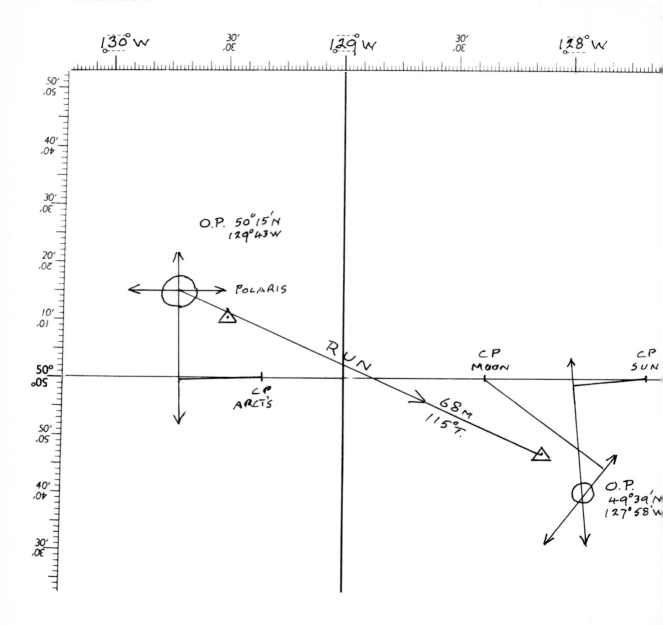

130° W   30'   129° W   30'   128° W
30'   30'

50'
.05

40'
.04

30'
.30

O.P. 50° 15' N
129° 43 W

20'
.20

POLARIS

10'
.01

RUN

50°
.05

CP
MOON

CP
SUN

CP
ARCT'S

68 M
115° T.

50'
.05

40'
.04

O.P.
49° 39' N
127° 58' W

30'
.30

108

c

RUN: 110°T Distance 17.5 M.

May 20th dawn – DR 49° 33' N. 127° 32' W.

Sights taken:

	MIRFAK.	ALTAIR	ARCTURUS
at GMT	11-53-40	11-54-10.	11-54-45.
GHA ♈ 11h	42° 28'.9	42° 28'.9	42° 28'.9
53-40	13° 27.2	54-10. 13° 34.7	54-45. 13° 43.5.
	55° 56.1	56° 03.6	56° 12.4.
	+ 360°	+ 360	+ 360
	415° 56.1	416° 03.6	416° 12.4.
C.P. Long: W –	127° 56.1	127° 03.6	127° 12.4.
LHA ♈	288°	289°	289°
C.P. Lat:	N 50°	N 50°	N 50°
	Hc 21° 10'	Hc 48° 13'	Hc 23° 59'
	Zn 036°	Zn 168°	Zn 272°
Sextant Alt:	21° 03'.9	48° 41'.5	24° 15'.6
I.E. –1.9			
Dip –2.4	– 4.3	– 4.3	– 4.3.
	20° 59.6	48° 37.2	24° 11.3.
Corn:	– 2.5	– 0.9	– 2.1
TRUE ALT:	20° 57.1	48° 36.3	24° 09.2
TAB: "	21° 10.0	48° 13.0	23° 59.0
Intercept.	AWAY 12.9	TO 23.3	TO 10.2

O.P. 49° 32' N. 127° 30' W.

Answers 3

Plotting sheet No. 5333 A

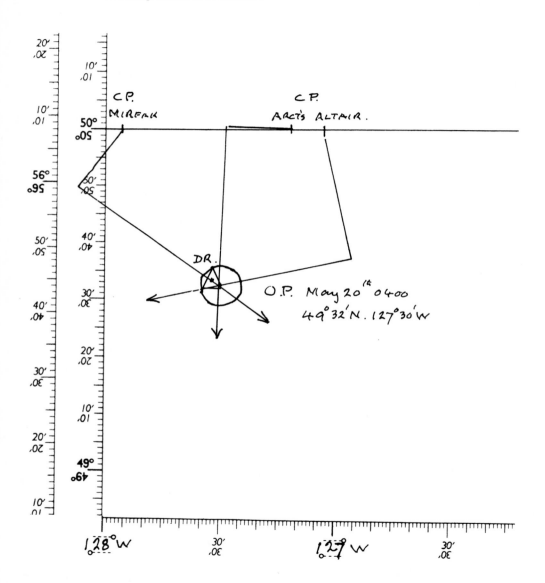

16

Off Capetown 34°S. 18°E
" Montevideo 35°S. 56°W.

<u>Great Circle Distance.</u>

	18°E			
	56°W			
D. Long:	74°	Log Hav:	9.55893	471
Lat:	S 34°	Log Cos:	9.91857	227
Lat:	S 35°	Log Cos:	9.91337	228
		Log Hav:	9.39087	
		= Nat. Hav:	.24596	456
* Lat ~ Lat:	1°	→ " "	.00008	398
			.24604	
		= 59°28'.4	= 3,568.4 M.	456

<u>Rhumbline Distance.</u>

Meridional Parts.

Lat:	34°S	=	2,158.39	143
Lat:	35°S		2,230.86	143
		D.M.P.	72.47	

Long: 18°E
" 56°W

D. Long:	74°	×60= 4,440' =	log	3.64738	164
D.M.P.		72.47 =	−log	1.86013	169
			log tan:	1.78725	} 294
		=	log sec:	1.78731	
D. Lat:	S 34° / S 35°	1° = 60' +	log	1.77815	167
			log	3.56546 = 3,677 M.	163.

<u>Gt. Circle Track shorter than Rhumbline by 108 M.</u>

*   <u>Same Name</u> (N or S) <u>subtract</u>
    <u>Contrary</u> " add ('Combine')

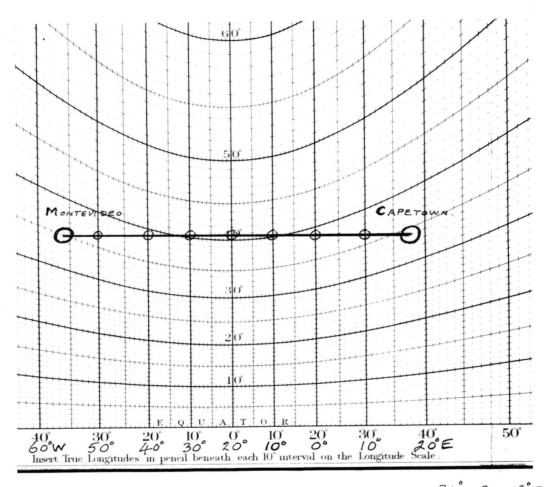

Insert True Longitudes in pencil beneath each 10° interval on the Longitude Scale.

Intermediate points along a Great Circle track

between 34°S. 18°E and 35°S. 56°W, at

intervals of 10° of longitude.

From Gt. Circle Diagram N° 5029.

34°	S	18° E
36° 30'	S	10° E
39°	S	0°
40° 15'	S	10° W
41°	S	20° W
40° 15'	S	30° W
39°	S	40° W
37°	S	50° W
35°	S	56° W

17   May   4th error 2^m 44^s Fast
May 11th error $\underline{2^m\ 54^s}$ Fast
10^s Gain
$10^s \div 7 = 1^s{\cdot}43$ per day Gain.
June 17th Error on May 11th, 2^m 54^s Fast
May 11–31 = 20
June 1–17 = $\underline{17}$
$\overline{37}$
37 days $\times$ $1^s{\cdot}43 = \underline{\qquad 53^s}$ Gain
Current error $\underline{3^m\ 47^s}$ Fast.

June 17th time by chronometer 08^h 14^m 45^s
Current error fast $\underline{-\quad 3\qquad 47}$
$\underline{08\ -10\ -58}$ GMT.

Answers 4

1 1975 Feb 16ᵗʰ DR 39°S 154°45′E.   MER: PASS.

Mer: Pass: 12·14 LMT.
DR. Long: in time, 154°45′E $\underline{-10\ 19}$
                            $\underline{01·55}$ GMT at DR.

$\underline{Sextant\ Alt}$: L.L. 63°43·1 N.
               IE. $-3·0$
               Dip. $\underline{-2·1}$ $-5·1$
                              $\overline{63°38·0}$

        Corr: $\underline{+15·7}$
TRUE ALT: 63°53·7 N
        from $\underline{90°}$
    T.Z.D.   26°06·3 S
$\underline{Dec}$: 01ʰ 12°36·4 S
d, $-0·9$ $\underline{-0·8}$ 12°35·6 S

    LAT: 38°41·9 S.

114

2

1975 Feb 17th 04-52-18 GMT. DR 45°50'S. 174°45'E. IE -2.5, HE 8 ft.

Check for GD   17^D 15-00 assumed LMT.
DR Long: in time, 174°45'E —   11 39
                    GD. 17^D 03-21 assumed GMT.
         ∴ USE 17^D 04-52-18 GMT

GHA 17^D 04^h   236°28'.4   S 12°13'.0
     52-18   13° 04.5 d.-0.9   — 0.8
                  249° 32.9.   S 12° 12'.2
CP. Long: E + 174° 27.1
              424°
            — 360
   LHA   64°
C.P. Lat: S 46°
   Dec: S 12° 12'

        Hc 26° 35'
   d + 43   + 9
TAB: ALT: 26° 44'

                180°
    Z   + 101°
            281° Zn.

Sextant Alt: L.L. 26° 20'.4
            IE -2.5
            Dip -2.7   — 5.2
                        26° 15.2
         Corr: + 14.3
    TRUE ALT: 26° 29.5
       TAB: -   26° 44.0
   Intercept: AWAY 14.5

C.P. 46°S 174°27'.1 E. Intercept: AWAY 14.5 Bearing 281°

3

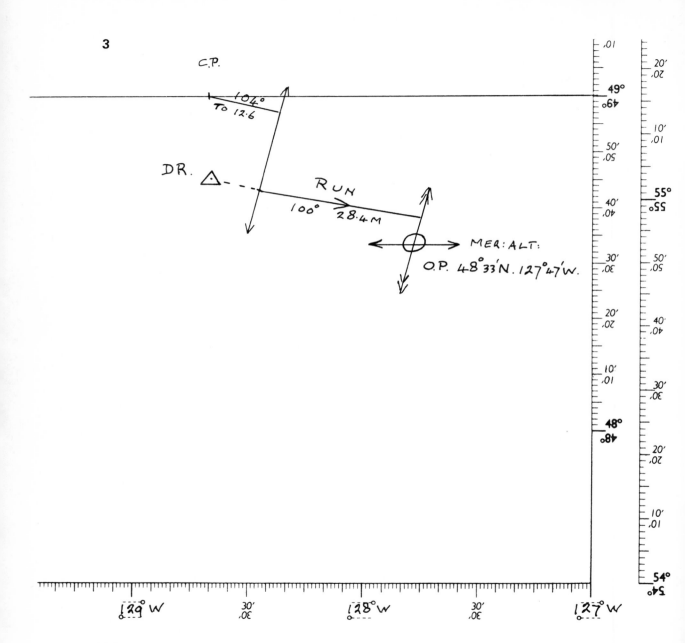

C.P.

104°
To 12·6

DR. △

RUN

100° 28·4 M

MER: ALT:
O.P. 48°33'N. 127°47'W.

49°
49°

.01

20'
20'

10'
.01

50'
05

55°
55°

40'
40'

30'
30'

50'
05

40'
40'

20'
.02

10'
.01

30'
30'

48°
48°

20'
.02

10'
.01

54°
54°

129° W   30'   128° W   30'   127° W
              30'   30'

116

4

Aug 30th in DR 35$°$S 172$°$E.

	C.Twilight	Sunrise	Sunset	C.Twilight	
30^D	05·57	06·23	17·39	18·05.	
DR.Long: 172$°$E −	11·28	−11·28	−11·28	−11·28	
29^D	18 29	29^D 18 55	30^D 06·11	30^D 06 37	GMT at DR.

5

May 20th DR 38$°$N. 125$°$W.   Dusk twilight

Civil Twilight in N 35$°$ 19·28   LMT.

$$\frac{40° \quad 19·43.}{}$$

change of 5$°$ + 15

∴   ˮ   ˮ   ˮ 1$°$ = + 3

∴   ˮ   ˮ   ˮ 3$°$ =   9^m

∴ in N 38$°$ = 19·28 + 9 = 20^D 19·37

DR Long: 125$°$W = + $\underline{\quad 8·20}$

use :   GD 21^D 03·57 GMT.

6

Draw a line across log book after last entry.
Enter new Zone Time, Z−12
Advance date by an extra day, viz:

July 4th $\dfrac{Z+12.}{23\ 45.}$

July 6th $\dfrac{Z−12.}{0001.}$

NO alteration to ship's clock or chronometer.

Answers 4

7   1975 Feb 15th 06-55-45 GMT.   DR 54°N. 5°20'E.   I.E. –4·0, HE 6 ft.

GHA Aries 06^h 234° 37'·6
        55-45   13° 58·5
                248° 36·1
DR. Long: E+   5° 20·
LHA ♈   253° 56'·1

<u>Sextant Alt</u>: POLARIS   53° 25'·0
          IE   – 4·0
          DIP –2·4   – 6·4
                  53° 18'·6
      Conn: – 0·7
                53° 17·9
        A$_0$ 1° 36·7
        A$_1$ ·6
        A$_2$ ·3
              54° 55·5
              – 1°
L AT: 53° 55'·5 N.

8

1975   Aug 31st DR 20°S. 87°E.   Dawn.   I.E. −0'.8, HE 6 ft.

Check for GD & GMT. Assume about 31^D 0550 LMT.
DR Long: in time, 87°E − <u>5 48</u>
GD. 31^D 00 02   assumed GMT.

chron: shows   11^h 52^m 09^s
∴ USE   GD. 30^D 23-52-09

GHA MARS 30^D 23^h 255° 28'.9   Dec: N 20° 50'.0
            52-09   13° 02.3   d, +0.3   <u>+ 0.3</u>
      V. 1.0   <u>0.9</u>   N 20° 50.3
                          268° 32.1
CP. Long: E + <u>87° 27.9</u>   <u>Sextant Alt: MARS. 48° 55'.7</u>
      LHA 356°   IE   −0.8
CP. Long: S 20°   Dip <u>−2.4</u>
      Dec: N 20° 50'   <u>−3.2</u>
                                              48° 52.5
      Hc   49° 49'   Corr: − 0.8
   d − 60   <u>− 50</u>   Addn'l Cor: <u>+ 0.1</u>
TAB: ALT: 48° 59'   TRUE ALT: 48° 51.8
                            TAB: "   <u>48° 59.0</u>
                         <u>Intercept: AWAY 7.2</u>
         180°
  Z   <u>−174°</u>
       006° = Zn.

<u>C.P. 20°S. 87°27'.9 E. Intercept: AWAY 7.2 Bearing 006°</u>

Answers 4

9

1975 Feb 17ᵗʰ Dawn - 38°50′S 167°E.

C. Twilight   17ᴰ 05·00 approx LMT.
DR Long: 167°E —   11 08.
G.D. 16ᴰ 17·52 approx. GMT at DR.

GHA. ARIES 16ᴰ 17ʰ   41° 03·8
                52ᵐ   13 02·1
                       54° 05·9

                                                    Zₙ.
DR Long. E+ 167°   ⎧ ANTARES   64° 54′   068°
    LHA 221° 05·9   ⎫   ⎨ ACRUX   58° 19′   210°
    Lat: S 39°   ⎭   ⎩ SPICA   56° 50′   322°

Sights taken: 1ˢᵗ   2ⁿᵈ   3ʳᵈ
                     ANTARES   ACRUX   SPICA.
    at GMT.   16ᴰ 17-52-24   17-53-02   17-53-41

GHA ARIES. 16ᴰ 17ʰ 41° 03·8   41° 03·8   41° 03·8.
        52-24 13° 08·2.   53-02 13° 17·7   53-41 13° 27·5.
               54° 12·0   54° 21·5   54° 31·3.
C.P. Long: E+166° 48·0   166° 38·5   166° 28·7.
    LHA ϒ 221°   221°   221°
C.P. Lat: S 39°   S 39°   S 39°

        Hc 64° 54′   Hc 58° 19′   Hc 56° 50′
        Zₙ 068°   Zₙ 210°   Zₙ 322°

Sextant Alt: 65° 29·7   58° 00·0   56° 32·2
IE −3·0
Dip −2·4
                  −5·4   −5·4   −5·4
                 65° 24·3   57° 54·6   56° 26·8.
    Conn: − 0·4   − 0·6   − 0·6
TRUE ALT: 65° 23·9   57° 54·0   56° 26·2
    TAB: ″ 64° 54·0   58° 19·0   56° 50·0
Intercept: TO 29·9   AWAY 25·0   AWAY 23·8.

            C.P. 38° 53 S. 167° 27′ E.

120

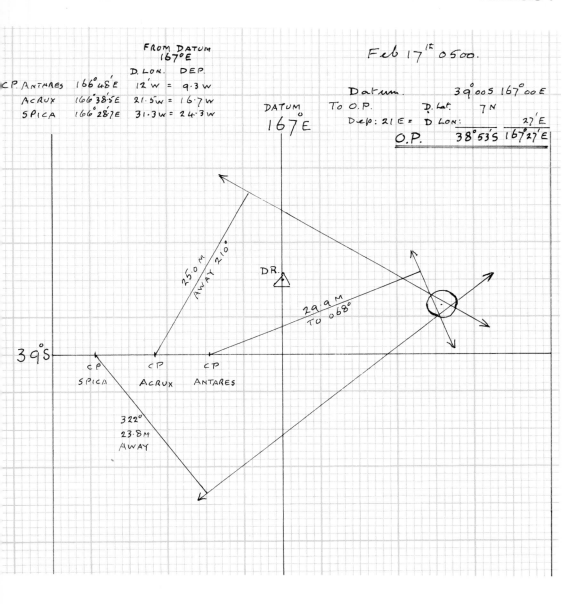

FROM DATUM
167°E

		D. LON.	DEP.
C.P. ANTARES	166° 48′ E	12′ W =	9·3 W
ACRUX	166° 38·5 E	21·5 W =	16·7 W
SPICA	166° 28·7 E	31·3 W =	24·3 W

DATUM
167°E

Feb 17ᵗʰ 0500.

Datum.		39° 00 S 167° 00 E
To O.P.	D. Lat.	7 N
Dep: 21 E =	D Lon:	27′ E
O.P.		38° 53′ S 167° 27′ E

DATUM
167°E

25·0 M
AWAY 210°

DR.

29·9 M
TO 068°

39°S

CP
SPICA

CP
ACRUX

CP
ANTARES

322°
23·8 M
AWAY

10

1975 Feb 16th p.m. chron: 1^h 53^m 49^s DR 50°15'S. 92°W. IE +3·0, HE 6 ft.

C. Twilight p.m. 16^D 19-55^{h} ^{m} LMT.
DR. Long: 92°W + _____6-08_____
            G.D. 17^D 02-03 GMT at DR.

∴ Use GD 17^D 01-53-49 GMT.

SHA Aldebaran   291° 22'·3   N 16° 27'·6
GHA Aries 17^D 01^h 161° 23·5
        53-49   _13° 29·5_
                   466° 15·3
C.P. Long: W - _92 15·3_
                 374°
                _-360_
LHA *   14°
C.P. Lat: S 50°
Dec: N 16° 28'

Hc   22° 51'
d -59   _-28_
TAB·ALT: 22° 23'

        180°
Z + _165_
    345° Zn.

Sextant Alt: ALDEBARAN 22° 21'·0
        IE +3·0
        Dip _-2·4_   _+0·6_
              22° 21·6
Conn: _-2·3_
TRUE ALT: 22° 19·3
TAB: "   22° 23·0
Intercept: AWAY 3·7

11

1975 May 21st evening. Chron: 10^h 53^m 34^s. DR 20°20'S. 88°E. IE −2.3, HE 8ft.

Check for GD. assume about 21^D 17 00 LMT.
DR Long: 88°E − 5 52.
GD 21^D 11·08 approx GMT.

∴ use 21^D 10-53-34 GMT.

GHA. MOON. 21^D 10^h 201° 19'3   Dec: S 7° 34'·2   H.P. 59.5
           53-34   12° 46·9   d +12·2   +10.9
v. 9.5   8·5   S 7° 45·1
          214° 14·7
C.P. Long: E+ 87° 45·3   Sextant Alt: MOON L.L. 31° 57'·4
    LHA.   302°   IE −2·3
C.P. Lat: S 20°   Dip −2·7   −5·0
   Dec: S 7° 45'   31° 52·4

                                    Corr: 58·1
    Hc 32° 24'   H.P. 59.5   7·0
d +20   + 15   TRUE ALT: 32° 57·5
TAB: ALT: 32° 39'   TAB: " 32° 39·0
                         Intercept: To 18·5

       180°
  Z − 94°
      086° Zn.

12

1975 Aug 29th in DR 44°S. 54°W.   Mer: Alt: MOON

Mer: Pass: 29ᴰ   05 10   ⊗ 29ᴰ   05 10
⊗ Corn: for Long: W   +   8   30ᴰ   06 01
Long: in time, 54°W   +   3 36   1 day = 360° =   + 51ᵐ
GD 29ᴰ   08 54 GMT.   ∴ 54°W = $\frac{54°}{360°}$ × 51ᵐ = 8 m.

Sextant Alt: MOON L.L.   25° 38.9 N.
IE −1.0
Dip −2.4   −3.4
25° 35.5
Corn: 60.6
HP. 55.7   2.7
TRUE ALT: 26° 38.8   N
from   90°
T. Z.D.   63° 21.2   S
Dec: 08ʰ 19° 28.9 N
d +4.2, 54ᵐ + 3.8   19° 32.7   N.
LAT: 43° 48.5 S

13

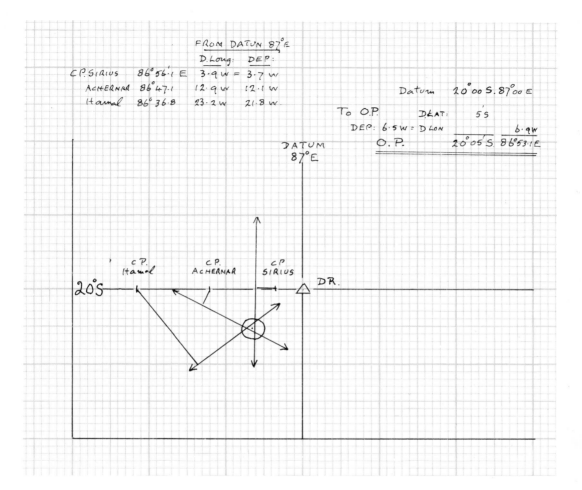

FROM DATUM 87°E

		D.Long.	DEP.
C.P. SIRIUS	86° 56·1 E	3·9 W =	3·7 W
ACHERNAR	86° 47·1	12·9 W	12·1 W
Hamal	86° 36.8	23·2 W	21·8 W

Datum   20° 00 S. 87° 00 E

TO O.P.   D.LAT: 5 S
DEP: 6·5 W = D LON   6·9 W

O.P.   20° 05 S   86° 53·1 E

DATUM
87°E

C.P.
Hamal

C.P.
ACHERNAR

C.P.
SIRIUS

DR.

20°S

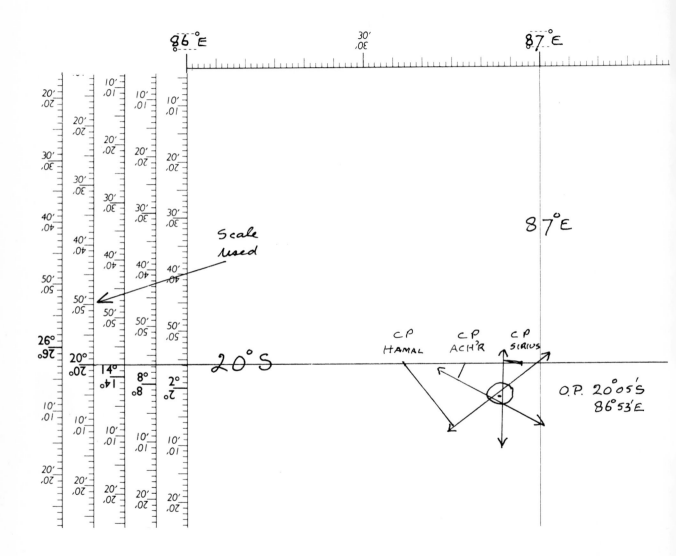

86° E   30'   87° E

87° E

Scale used

20° S

CP
HAMAL

CP
ACH'R

CP
SIRIUS

O.P. 20°05'S
86°53'E

14

Compass Check: Feb 15th pm. DR. 46°41'S 167°20'E.

assume about 1600 LMT

DR. Long: E — 11 09

   04 51   assumed GMT at DR.

∴ use 15^D 05-53-50 GMT.

GHA. 15^D 05^h	251° 26'8	Dec: S 12° 53'5
53-50	13° 27·5	d-0·9 — 0·8
	264° 54·3.	S 12° 52·7
C. P. Long E+167° 05·7		
	432°	
	— 360°	
LHA	72°	
Lat: S 47°		
Dec: S 12°53		

            180°
Z + 095°
           275° Zm.

Azimuth   275° T.
 Variation   — 12°E
            263° M.
By steering compass 271° C
∴ Deviation = 8°W.   (On ship's heading at the time.)

            Variation   12° E
            Deviation   8° W.
            Total Error 4° E

Answers 4

15.a

1975 Feb. 16th   DR. 17°10'N. 58°15'W.

Dawn c. Twilight   06.05   LMT.
DR Long: 58°15'W   + 3.53
                       0958 GMT at DR.
        Use 0955 (to suit the extracts from N.A)

GHA ARIES 09h   280° 44·1
          55m   13 47·3   approx:
                 294° 31·4   Alt.   Bearing
  C.P. Long:W – 58° 31·4   ⎰ ALTAIR   29° 49'   089°
  LHA ♈   236°   ⎱ SPICA   45° 27   233°
  C.P. Lat: N 17°   ⎰ Alkaid   49° 50   330°

<u>Sights taken:</u>

	1st	2nd	3rd
	ALTAIR	SPICA	Alkaid.
at G.M.T.	09-52-15	09-52-48	09-53-10.

GHA Aries 09h   280° 44·1   280° 44·1   280° 44·1
         52-15.   13° 05·9   52-48. 13° 14·2   53-10. 13° 19·7
                 293° 50·0   293° 58·3   294° 03·8
  C.P. Long:W – 57° 50·0   – 57° 58·3   – 58° 03·8.
  LHA ♈   236°   236°   236°
  C.P. Lat: N 17°   N 17°   N 17°.

     Hc 29° 49'   Hc 45° 27'   Hc 49° 50'
     Zn 089°   Zn 233°   Zn 330°

<u>Sextant Alt:</u> 29° 52·5   45° 22·7   50° 06·0
     I.E. –4·0
     Dip –2·7   –6·7   –6·7   –6·7
               29° 45·8   45° 16·0   49° 59·3
     Corr: –1·7   –1·0   – 0·8.
     TRUE ALT: 29° 44·1   45° 15·0   49° 58·5
     TAB: 29° 49·0   45° 27·0   49° 50·0
<u>Intercept:</u> AWAY 4·9   AWAY 12·0   TO 8·5

<u>O.P. 17°15'N. 57°55'W.</u>

Plotting sheet No. 5331 A

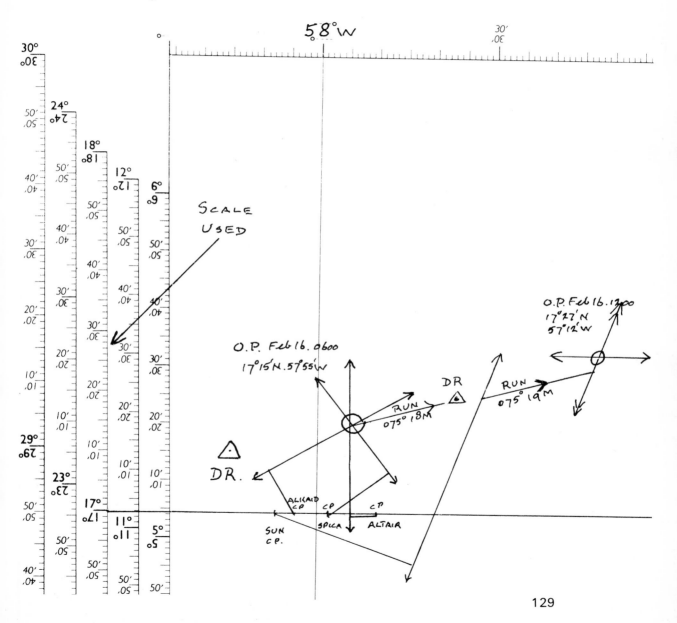

129

Answers 4

b

O.P. 17°15'N 57°55'W   at Feb 16ʰ 0600.

<u>RUN</u>:   Co 075°T   18M.

Feb: 16ʰ   11-54-37 GMT.   DR. 17° 19·5 N. 57°37'W.

```
G.H.A 16ᴰ 11ʰ  341° 27·7   Dec: S 12° 27·8
     54-37     13° 39·3   d-0·9    -0·8
              355° 07·0           S 12° 27·0
C.P. Long: W- 58° 07·0
     L.H.A. 297°
C.P. Lat:  N 17°
     Dec:  S 12° 27'
```

```
Hc      21° 20'
d.-24    -11
TAB: ALT: 21° 09'

Z  111° = Zn.
```

Sextant Alt: LL. 21° 25·7
IE & Dip   -6·7
     21° 19·0
Corn: +13·5
TRUE ALT: 21° 32·5
TAB: "   21° 09·0
<u>Intercept</u>: <u>To 23·5</u>

c

<u>RUN</u>   Co 075°T   19M.   DR 57°14'W apprx.

Feb: 16ʰ   Mer: Pass: 12 14   LMT
DR Long: 57°14'W +   3 49
         16 03   GMT at DR.

```
Sextant Alt: L.L.  60° 00·6  S
      IE & Dip      -6·7
                   59° 53·9
      Corn:        +15·7
   TRUE ALT:  60° 09·6  S
      from    90°
      T.Z.D.  29° 50·4  N
    Dec: 16ʰ  12° 23·4  S
      LAT:    17° 27·0  N
```

O.P. 17°27'N. 57°12'W.

d　　RUN : Co 080°T　34 M.　DR. 17°33'N. 56°38'W.

Feb 16th

	MOON	VENUS	RIGEL.
at GMT.	21-54-11.	21-54-58	21-55-32.

Cr HA.　74°58'4　N14°04'8　108°09'3　54°22'1　SHA 281°39'5　58°13'9.
　　　　 12°55'7 d8·9　+ 8·1　13°44'5 d-1·3　-1·2　GHA ♈ 101°13'7
v. 13·2　　12·0　N14°12·9　v-0·4　-0·4　54°20·9　　13 55·3.
　　　　 88°06·1　　　　　121°53·4　　　　396°48·5
C.P. Long: W-56°06·1　　　- 56°53·4　　　- 56°48·5
　LHA　32°　　　　　　65°　　　　　340°
C.P. Lat: N18°　　　　N 18°　　　　N 18°
　Dec: N14°13'　　　S 4°21'　　　S 8°14'

　Hc　59°01'　　Hc 22°18'　　Hc 57°21'
d +12　　+ 3　　d -22　　- 8　　d -48　　- 11.
TAB: ALT: 59°04'　　　22°10'　　　57°10'
　　　　 360°　　　　 360°
　Z　 - 93　　　　- 102
　　　 267° = Zn　　258° = Zn.　　141° = Zn

Sextant Alt: L.L. 58°57'9　　22°08'2　　57°49'3
　I E & Dip　　- 6·7　　　-6·7　　　-6·7
　　　　 58°51·2　　22°01·5　　57°42·6
　　Corr: + 39·9　　　-2·4　　　- 0·6
H.P 55·1　　2·9

　TRUE ALT: 59°34·0　　21°59·1　　57°42·0
　TAB: "　59°04·0　　22°10·0　　57°10·0
Intercept :　TO　30·0　　AWAY 10·9　　TO　32·0.

O.P. 17°31'N. 56°35'W.

Plotting sheet No. 5331 A

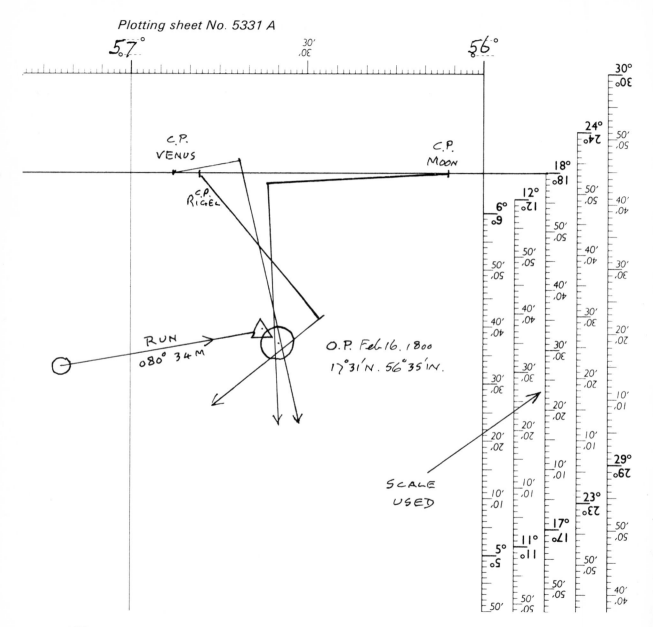

C.P.
VENUS

C.P.
MOON

C.P.
RIGEL

RUN
080° 34 M

O.P. Feb 16. 1800
17°31'N. 56°35'N.

SCALE
USED

57°

30'
.30'

56°

30°

24°

18°

12°

6°

5°

11°

17°

23°

29°

16

Positions   34°S 18°E   and   51°S 57°W.

GREAT CIRCLE DISTANCE.   *

Long:	18°E		
	57°W		
D. Long:	75°	log Hav: 9·56889	472
Lat:	34°S	log Cos: 9·91857	227
Lat:	51°S.	log Cos: 9·79887	244
		log Hav: 9·28633	
		= Nat: Hav: ·19334	449
Lat ~ Lat: 17° →		" " ·02185	
		– " ·21519	
		= 55°16'·6 =	3,317 M	452.

RHUMBLINE DISTANCE.

Meridional Parts.

Lat 34°S =	2,158·39	143
" 51°S =	3,550·60	145
D. M.P.	1,392·21	

D. Long: 75° = 4,500' = log 3·65321		164
D. M.P. 1,392·2 = –log 3·14364		159
log tan: 0·50957		} 265
= log sec: 0·52942		
D. Lat. 17° = 1,020' = log 3·00860.		159
log. 3·53802 = 3,452 M.		163.

RHUMBLINE EXCEEDS Gt. CIRCLE BY 135 M.

* ALTERNATIVELY, USING NP 401, H.O.229 on H.D 486

L. H.A. (= D. Long)	75°	Hc = 34° 43'	
Lat: (= Lat:)	51°	CZD = 55° 17'	
Dec: (= Lat:)	34°	= 3,317 Miles	

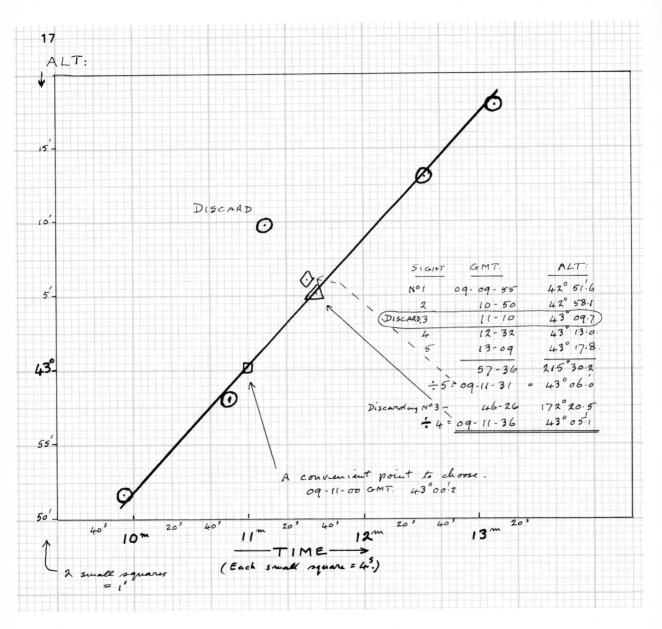

17

ALT:

DISCARD

SIGHT	GMT.	ALT:
N°1	09- 09 - 55	42° 51.6
2	10 - 50	42° 58.1
DISCARD 3	11 - 10	43° 09.7
4	12 - 32	43° 13.0
5	13 - 09	43° 17.8
	57 - 36	215° 30.2
÷ 5 = 09-11-31		= 43° 06.0
Discarding N°3 -	46 - 26	172° 20.5
÷ 4 = 09 - 11 - 36		43° 05.1

15'

10'

5'

43°

A convenient point to choose.
09 - 11 - 00 GMT. 43° 00.2

55'

50'

40ˢ   10ᵐ   20ˢ   40ˢ   11ᵐ   20ˢ   40ˢ   12ᵐ   20ˢ   40ˢ   13ᵐ   20ˢ

— TIME —
(Each small square = 4ˢ.)

2 small squares
= 1'

134

Answers 5

1   1975   Aug 31ˢᵗ   Sun Mer: Alt: DR. 47°20'N. 133°45'W.

      Mer: Pass: 12 00   LMT.
    DR. Long: in time, 133°45'W $\underline{+ \; 8 \; 55}$
                     20 55   GMT at D.R. (by chronometer)
   Ship's clock recording
          Z+9. $\underline{- 9 \; 00.}$
            $\underline{11 \; 55}$ time by ship's clock.

    $\underline{\text{Sextant Alt:}}$ L.L.   50° 59'.2 . S
             IE −2.0
           Dip $\underline{-2.7}$ $\underline{-4.7}$
                  50° 54.5
         Corr: $\underline{+ 15.2.}$
      TRUE ALT: 51° 09.7   S
         from $\underline{90°}$
       T.Z.D.   38° 50.3 . N
   $\underline{\text{Dec: 20ʰ}}$ 8°39.0 N
d,−0.9, 55ᵐ $\underline{− 0.8}$ 8° 38.2   N

      $\underline{\underline{\text{LAT: } 47° 28'.5 \text{ N.}}}$

2

1975 May 21st 4^h 55^m 14^s. DR 48°45'N. 128°40'W. IE. -2.8, HE 8 ft.

Check for GD and time.

assume 21^D 08 00 LMT

DR. Long: in Time, 128°40'w + 8 35.

GD. 21^D 16 35 approx GMT

∴ Time 21^D 16-55-14 GMT.

GHA 16^h 60° 52'.2   Dec: N 20° 08'.9

55-14   13° 48.5   d,+0.5   +0.5

74° 40.7   N 20° 09.4

+360

434° 40.7

CP. Long: W -128° 40.7

LHA   306°

CP. Lat: N 49°   Sextant Alt: L.L. 38° 31.3

Dec: N 20° 09'   IE -2.8

Dip -2.7   -5.5

38° 25.8

Hc 38° 21'   Corn: +14.8

d, + 44   + 7.   TRUE ALT: 38° 40.6

TAB: ALT: 38° 28'   TAB: " 38° 28.0.

Z 104° = Zn.   Intercept: To 12.6

C.P. 49° N. 128° 40'.7 W. Intercept: To 12.6, bearing 104°.

3.a

1975 Feb 15th DR. 47° 10'S. 166° 55'E.

Mer: Pass: 15^D 12·14   LMT.
DR. Long: 166°55'E —   11·08
                                    01·06   GMT at DR. — chronometer

Clock set to   Z — 11. + 11
Zone Time   12 06   by ship's clock.

c

O.P.   46° 42'S. 167° 25'E.

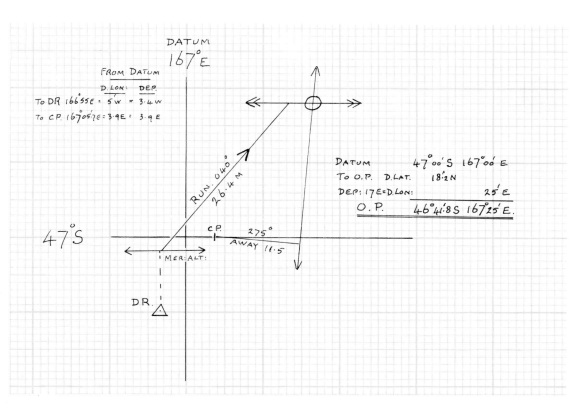

DATUM
167° E

FROM DATUM
D. LON: DEP.
To DR 166°55'E = 5'W = 3·4 W
To C.P. 167°05·7E = 3·9E = 3·9 E

RUN. 040°
26·4 M

DATUM   47° 00'S 167° 00'E
To O.P.   D. LAT.   18'·2 N
DEP: 17 E = D. LON: 25' E
O.P.   46° 41·8 S 167° 25'E.

47°S

C.P.   275°
AWAY 11·5

MER: ALT:

DR.

4

Moonrise and Moonset on May 20/21st in 22°S 88°E.

	MOON RISE	MOON SET.		RISE	SET
May. 20°S	20^D 13·49	21^D 02·27	20°S	1349	0227 (21st)
Corr: for 2°S	− 1 a)	− 1 a)	30°S	1346	0232 "
Corr: for Long: 88°E	− 11 b)	− 14 b)	diff: 10°	− 3	− 5
	20^D 13·37	21^D 02·12 LMT.	∴ 2° =	− 1^m	− 1^m a)
DR Long: in time, 88°E	− 5·52	− 5·52			
G.D.	20^D 07·45	20^D 20·20 G.MT.			

in 20°S

	RISE	SET
20^D	1349	0227 (21st)
19^D	1306	0128 "

1 day on 360° = −43 , −59

∴ 88°E = $\frac{88}{360} \times 43^m$ $\frac{88}{360} \times 59^m$

= 11^m = 14^m

b)   b)

5

Aug 29th DR. 32°30'N. 64°W.

assume local time about 29^D 09·00 LMT.

DR Long: 64°W   + 4·16

29^D 13·16 assumed GMT.

Read chron: as GD. 29^D 13-09-45

D.W.E. Slow + 7·34

Use for sight: 29^D 13-17-19 G.MT.

6

July 3rd $\dfrac{Z-12}{22\cdot30}$

July 3rd $\dfrac{Z+12}{00\cdot30}$

Line drawn across page after last
entry before midnight.
Fresh Zone, Z+12 entered,
Date brought down UNCHANGED.

Ship's clock and chronometer
left UNALTERED.

7

1975 May 19ᵗʰ   07-52-15 GMT.   DR. 44°N. 65°30′W.

IE −1.5, HE. 8 ft.

GHA ARIES 07ʰ   341° 19.9
          52-15   13° 05.9
                 354° 25.8
D.R. Long: W − 65° 30
LHA. Υ   288° 55.8

Sextant Alt: POLARIS   44° 09.1
                IE.   −1.5
                Dip   −2.7   − 4.2
                              44° 04.9
                Corr: − 1.0
                              44° 03.9
                A₀   1° 10.8
                A₁   .5
                A₂   .3
                      45° 15.5
                      − 1°
LAT: 44° 15′.5 N.

139

8

1975 May 20th 4^h 54^m 37^s D.R. 47°N 134°W. IE −2.0, Ht 8 ft.

Check GD. assume 20^D 2000 LMT.
D.R. Long: 134°W + 8 56
GD. 21^D 0456 assumed GMT

Use GD. 21^D 04−54−37 GMT.

GHA Venus 21^D 04^h 194° 11.3   Dec: N 25° 24.1
       54−37   13° 39.3   d −0.2   −0.2
v. −0.6   − 0.5   N 25° 23.9
                    207° 50.1

C.P. Long: W −133 50.1   Sextant Alt: VENUS. 29° 13.7
    L H A.   74°   IE −2.0
C P. Lat: N 47°   Dip −2.7   −4.7
   Dec: N 25° 24'   29° 09.0
                                  Corr,   − 1.7
     Hc   28° 39'   Addn'l Cor: + 0.1
   d +40   +16   TRUE ALT: 29° 07.4
 TAB: ALT: 28° 55'   TAB: "   28° 55.0
                          Intercept: TO   12.4
             360°
    Z − 83
         277° Zn.

9

1975 Feb 17[15]   DR 32° 15'N 25° 15'W.

<u>Plan</u>.   dusk twilight 17[D] 18 11 LMT.
            DR. Long: 25° 15'w +   1 41
                              17[D] 19 52 GMT at DR.

GHA Aries 19[h] 72° 07.9
           52[m] 13° 02.1
                 85° 10.0
    CP Long: W − 25° 10.0
         LHA ♈ 60°   }
    CP Lat: N 32°

POLLUX	41° 57'	079°
PROCYON	32° 38'	106°
SIRIUS	27° 27'	135°
RIGEL	46° 08	153°

<u>Observed</u>

	POLLUX	PROCYON	SIRIUS	RIGEL
at GMT	19-53-25	19-54-10	19-54-50	19-55-15
GHA Aries	72° 07.9	72° 07.9	72° 07.9	72° 07.9
Incr:	13° 23.4	13° 34.7	13° 44.8	13° 51.0
	85° 31.3	85° 42.6	85° 52.7	85° 58.9
CP. Long: W	−25° 31.3	25° 42.6	25° 52.7	25° 58.9
LHA	60°	60°	60°	60°
CP. Lat:	N 32°	N 32°	N 32°	N 32°
Hc	41° 57'	32° 38'	27° 27'	46° 08'
Zm	079°	106°	135°	153°

<u>Sextant Alt:</u>

	POLLUX	PROCYON	SIRIUS	RIGEL
Sextant Alt:	41° 57.2	32° 41.8	27° 33.3	46° 10.1
IE −0.8 Dip −2.4	−3.2	−3.2	−3.2	−3.2
	41° 54.0	32° 38.6	27° 30.1	46° 06.9
Corr:	−1.1	−1.5	−1.9	−0.9
TRUE ALT:	41° 52.9	32° 37.1	27° 28.2	46° 06.0
TAB: "	41° 57.0	32° 38.0	27° 27.0	46° 08.0
<u>Intercept</u>:	AWAY 4.1	AWAY 0.9	TO 1.2	AWAY 2.0

<u>O.P. 32° 10'N. 25° 39'W.</u>

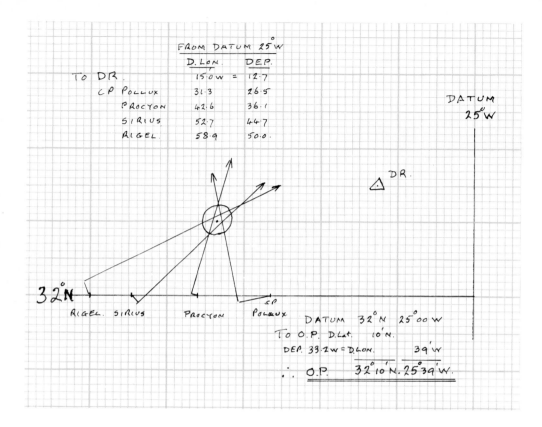

FROM DATUM 25°W

	D. LON.		DEP.
TO DR.	15·0 W	=	12·7
CP POLLUX	31·3		26·5
PROCYON	42·6		36·1
SIRIUS	52·7		44·7
RIGEL	58·9		50·0

DATUM
25°W

DR.

32°N

RIGEL.   SIRIUS   PROCYON   SP POLLUX

DATUM   32°N 25°00 W

TO O.P. D.Lat.   10'N.

DEP. 33·2 w = D.LON.   39' w

∴ O.P.   32°10'N. 25°39'W.

10

1975   Aug 29ᵗʰ 07-53-12 GMT.   DR 34°10'S 152°E.   I.E.-4.2, HE 8ft.

Check for GD. assume 29ᴰ 1800 LMT.
   DR Long: 152°E — 1008
               GD 29ᴰ 0752   assumed GMT at DR.

SHA Altair   62°35.6   N 8°48.5
GHA Aries 07ʰ 81°52.1
   Incr: 53-12. 13°20.2
      GHA *   157°47.9
CP. Long: E+152°12.1
      LHA *   310°
CP. Lat: S 34°
   Dec: N 8°48'

      Hc 26°44'
   d -42   -34
TAB: ALT: 26°10'

         180°
   Z   -122
         058° Zn.

Sextant Alt: ALTAIR. 26°10.4
               IE.-4.2
               Dip -2.7   -6.9
                         26°03.5
            Conn: -2.0
         TRUE ALT 26°01.5
            TAB: .. 26°10.0
Intercept.   AWAY 8.5

C.P. 34°S 152°12.1 E. Intercept. AWAY 8.5, Bearing 058°.

11

1975 May 19ᵗʰ   DR. 46°15'N. 132°30'W.   IE −2'·0, HE. 10 ft

19ᴰ 16 00   approx Z + 9 time.

$$\begin{array}{r} Z \quad + 9 \\ \hline GD \quad 20^D \quad 01 \quad 00 \end{array}$$ approx GMT.

chron: 00 - 53 - 37   GMT.

GHA Moon. 20ᴰ 00ʰ 68° 55'·6 Dec: S 0° 20'·4   H.P. 59'·5.
  53-37   12° 47·6 d +13·0 +11·6.
v. 10·2   ───────   S 0° 32'·0
         9·1
       ──────
       81° 52·3
       +360
       ───────
       441° 52·3   Sextant Alt: Moon U.L. 24° 55'·4
CP. Long: W − 132° 52·3   IE −2·0
  LHA   309°   Dip −3·1   −5·1
CP. Lat: N 46° ,   ─────────
  Dec: S 0° 32   24° 50·3.
                        Corn: 60·9.
  Hc   25° 55'   H.P. 59'·5 U.L.   4·7
  d. −48   −26   25° 55·9.
TAB: ALT: 25° 29'   . for U.L.   −30·0.
                        TRUE ALT: 25° 25·9
  Z   120° = Zn   TAB: .. 25° 29·0
                    Intercept: AWAY 3·1

C.P. 46°N. 132°52'·3 W. Intercept: AWAY 3·1, bearing 120°

144

12

1975 May 20th   DR. 51°N. 127°W.

Moon Mer: Pass: 20^D 2006
Corr: for Long: 127°W + _____18_____
                    20^D 2024
DR Long: in time, 127°W + _____8 28_____
Mer: Pass: at DR. GD 21^D 04 52 GMT. ☒

Corr: for Long:
    20^D 2006
    21^D 2058.
1 day = 360° = + 52^m
127°W = $\frac{127}{360}$ × 52^m = _18 m._

Sextant Alt: MOON L.L. 31° 40'.9 S
          I E. −1.7
          Dip −2.7   −4.4
                    31° 36.5
          Corr: 58.2.
     H.P. 59.5   7.0
     TRUE ALT: 32° 41.7   S.
          from 90°
          T.Z.D. 57° 18.3 N.
Dec: 21^D 04^h 6° 19'.95
d.+12.4 52^m +10.9 6° 30.8 S

     LAT: 50° 47'.5 N

☒   Alternative method, to nearest second:

req^d L H A Moon   0°
          DR Long: W +127°
          ∴ GHA req^d 127°

          GHA   114° 27.6 = 04^h
          remainder 12° 32.4
          v. 9.7, 51^m _____8.3_____
                    12° 24.1 = 51^m 58^s

          Mer: Pass 21^D 04−51−58 GMT.

13

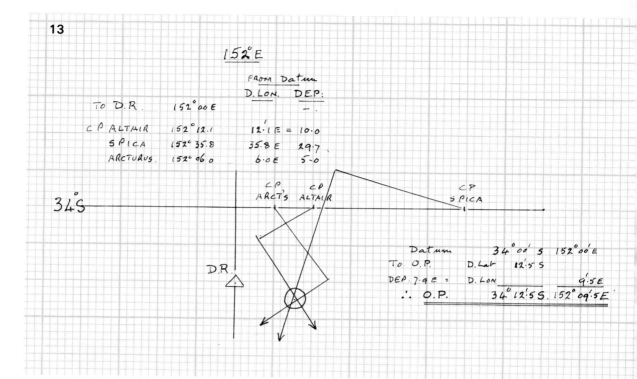

152°E

FROM Datum

		D. LON.	DEP:
TO D.R.	152° 00 E		-.
CP ALTAIR	152° 12.1	12.1 E =	10.0
SPICA	152° 35.8	35.8 E	29.7
ARCTURUS.	152° 06.0	6.0 E	5.0

34°S

CP ARCT'S   CP ALTAIR   CP SPICA

D.R

	Datum	34° 00' S	152° 00' E
TO O.P.	D. Lat	12.5 S	
DEP. 7.9 E =	D. Lon		9.5 E
∴ O.P.		34° 12.5 S.	152° 09.5 E

14

Compass Check 1975 May 21ˢᵗ - 11-53-56 GMT. DR 10°20'N. 65°30'E.

GHA 11ʰ   345° 52'·4   Dec: N 20° 06'·4
53·56   13° 29·0   d, +0·5   + 0·4
           359° 21·4   N 20° 06·8
CP Long. E+ 65° 38·6
           425°
           -360
LHA   065°
CP. Lat: N 10°
  Dec: N 20° 07'

        360°
Z   -   73°
        287° Zm

Sun's Azimuth   287° T
     Variation   3° W
                     290° M
By steering Compass 287° C
∴ Deviation   3° E

        Var: 3° W
        Dev: 3° E
TOTAL ERROR   0°

15

1975 Feb 16th D.R. 39°20'S. 143°30'E

Check for G.D.   16^D 07-55   Ship's time
Z   −10
G.D. 15^D 21 55   approx GMT
By chron: (15^D) 21-54-13 GMT.

G.H.A 15^D 21^h 131° 27'3   Dec: S 12°39'8
54-13.   13° 33.3   d−0.9   −0.8.
145° 00.6.   S 12° 39'0

C.P. Long: E+143° 59.4.
L.H.A   289°
C.P. Lat: S 39°
Dec: S 12° 39'0

Hc   22° 14'
d + 36   + 23
TAB: ALT: 22° 37'
180°
Z − 92°
088° Zn

Sextant Alt: L.L.   22° 09'2
IE −3.0
Dip −3.1   − 6.1
22° 03.1
Corn: + 13.9
TRUE ALT: 22° 17.0.
TAB: "   22° 37.0.
Intercept: AWAY 20.0.

R U N :   080°T.   22 M.

New D.R.   39° 16'S.   144° 02'E.

Mer: Pass   12 14
D.R. Long: 146° E − 9 36.
G.D 16^D 02 38 GMT.

Sextant Alt: L.L. 63° 08'5   N
IE & Dip   −6.1
63° 02.4
Corn: + 15.7
TRUE ALT: 63° 18.1   N
from 90°
26° 41.9   S
Dec: 16^D 02^h 12°35.5 S
d, −0.9 38^m −0.5   12° 35.0   S
LAT: 39° 16.9   S.

O.P.   39° 17'S. 144° 03'E.

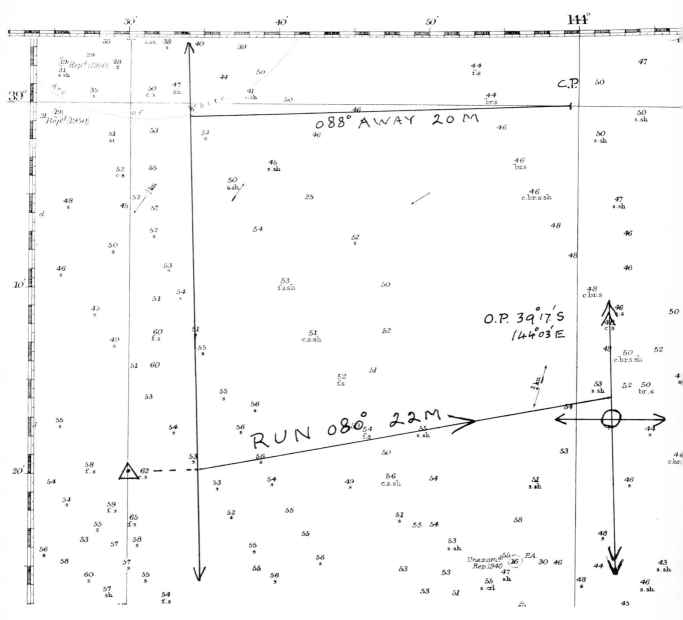

b

Distance covered between $15^D 22^h$ and $16^D 0238$ (GMT) $4\frac{1}{2}$ hrs - 22 M

= about 5 km.

p.m. C. Twilight Feb 16^D 1930 LMT

DR Long: $144°E$ $\underline{\quad -936\quad}$

16^D 09.54 GMT.

Mer. Alt. at 16^D $\underline{\quad 02.38\quad}$ "

Time elapsed since $\overline{7^h 16^m}$ at 5 kn, say 36 M. Co $085°T$.

O.P. at Mer. Pass. was $39°17'S$ $144°03'E$

∴ D.R. at p.m. C. Twilight $39°14'S$ $144°49'E$ by plot.

Pre-calc:

GHA Υ 16^D 09^h $280°44'.1$

54^m $\underline{\quad 13°32.2\quad}$

$294°16.3$

Selected Stars ♦

C.P. Long $E+143°43.7$

$\underline{\quad\quad\quad}$

$438°$

		Zn.
SIRIUS	$59°59'$	$048°$
ACRUX	$26°43$	$151°$
Diphda	$28°39$	$269°$

LHA = $78°$ }

Lat: S$39°$ }

Stars Observed:	SIRIUS	ACRUX	Diphda
at GMT	09-53-33	09-54-05	09-54-37
GHA Υ 09^h	$280°44'.1$	$280°44'.1$	$280°44'.1$
53-33.	$\underline{13°25.4}$	54-05 $\underline{13°33.5}$	54-37 $\underline{13°41.5}$
	$294°09.5$	$294°17.6$	$294°25.6$
C.P. Long: E+	$\underline{144°50.5}$	$+\underline{144°42.4}$	$+\underline{144°34.4}$
	$439°$	$439°$	$439°$
	$\underline{-360°}$	$\underline{-360°}$	$\underline{-360°}$
LHA Υ	$79°$	$79°$	$79°$
C.P. Lat:	S$39°$	S$39°$	S$39°$
	Hc $60°33.$ Zn $047°$	Hc $27°06'$ Zn $151°$	Hc $27°52'$ Zn $269°$

Sextant Alt:	$60°31'.7$	$27°31'.3$	$27°44'.3.$
I.E. -3.0			
Dip. -3.1	$\underline{-6.1}$	$\underline{-6.1}$	$\underline{-6.1}$
	$60°25.6$	$27°25.2$	$27°38.2.$
Corr:	$\underline{-0.6}$	$\underline{-1.9}$	$\underline{-1.8}$
TRUE ALT:	$60°25.0$	$27°23.3$	$27°36.4$
TAB: "	$60°33.0$	$27°06.0$	$27°52.0.$
Intercept:	AWAY 8.0	TO 17.3	AWAY 15.6.

O.P. $39°15'S$ $144°54.5E$

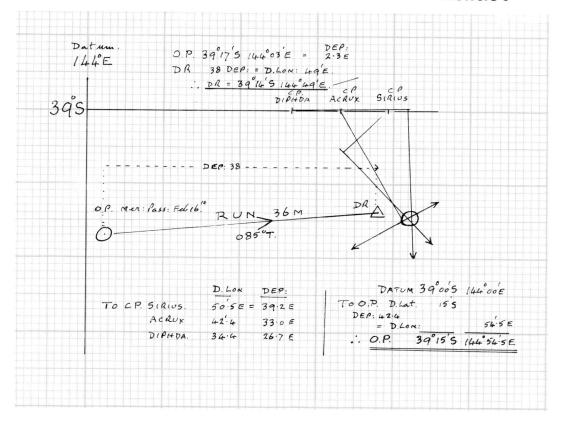

Datum.
144°E

39°S

O.P. 39°17'S 144°03'E = DEP: 2·3 E
DR   38 DEP: = D.Lon: 49'E.
∴ DR = 39°16'S 144°49'E.

C.P.   C.P.   C.P.
DIPHDA   ACRUX   SIRIUS

DEP: 38

O.P. Mer: Pass: Feb 16ᵗʰ   DR
RUN   36 M
085° T.

	D.Lon	DEP:
TO C.P. SIRIUS.	50·5 E =	39·2 E
ACRUX	42'·4	33·0 E
DIPHDA.	34·4	26·7 E

DATUM 39°00'S 144°00'E
TO O.P. D.Lat.   15 S
DEP: 42·4
= D.Lon: 54·5 E
∴ O.P.   39°15'S 144°54·5E

Answers 5

15.c

O.P. Feb 16ᵗ pm twilight 39° 15' S 144° 54·5' E.

<u>RUN</u> Co. 068°T 44 M.

D.R. 38° 58' S 145° 46' E.   Check your G.D. a.m. C.Twilight 17ᴰ 0500.

D.R. Long: <u>−9.44</u>
G.D. 16ᴰ 1916 GMT

<u>Sights taken:</u>   MARS   ACRUX   SPICA
at GMT. 16ᴰ +8-53-49   18-54-08   18-54-47.

		MARS		ACRUX	SPICA
G.H.A. Mars	125° 14·9	522° 48·3	γ 56° 06·3	56° 06·3.
ꞮꞏuꝈ:	13° 27·3 d−0·2	−·2.	13° 34·2	13° 44·0.
v. 0·5		·4 522° 48·1		
	138° 42·6		69° 40·5	69° 50·3
C.P. Long: E+	145° 17·4		145° 19·5	145° 9·7
	284°		215°	215°
C.P. Lat: S 39°			S 39°	S 39°
Dec: S 22° 48'				

Hc 24° 13'
d, +33   +26
TAB. ALT: 24° 39'   Hc 60° 30'   Hc 59° 22'

180°
Z −81°
099° Zn.   206° Zn.   332° Zn.

	MARS	ACRUX	SPICA
<u>Sextant Alt:</u>	25° 06·2.	60° 22·9	59° 22·1
I.E. −3·0			
Dip −3·1	−6·1	−6·1	−6·1
	25° 00·1	60° 16·8	59° 16·0.
Corr:	−2·1	−0·6	−0·6
TRUE ALT:	24° 58·0	60° 16·2	59° 15·4
TAB: "	24° 39·0.	60° 30·0	59° 22·0
<u>Intercept:</u>	TO 19·0	AWAY 13·8	AWAY 6·6.

<u>O.P. 38° 54' S. 145° 43' E.</u>

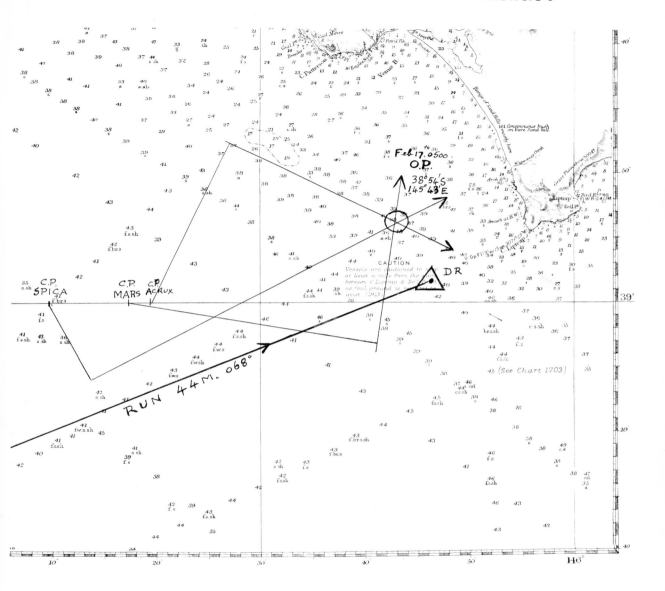

Feb 17. 0500.
O.P.
38°54'S
145°43'E

CAUTION
Vessels are cautioned to keep
at least a mile from the shore
between C. Liptrap & Bell's
as foul ground is marked
about 1943

DR

C.P.
SPICA

C.P.
MARS

C.P.
ACRUX

RUN 44M. 068°

(See Chart 1703)

16

$38° N \ 145° E \qquad$ and $\qquad 48° N \ 128° W$.

<u>Great Circle Track.</u>   *

$145° E \ \& \ 128° W = 273°$
$\qquad$ from $\underline{360}$

D. Long:	$87°$	log Hav.	$9 \cdot 67562$	
Lat.	N $38°$	log Cos.	$9 \cdot 89653$	
Lat.	N $48°$	log Cos.	$\underline{9 \cdot 82551}$	
		log Haw.	$9 \cdot 39766$	
		= Nat. Hav.	$\cdot 24984$	
Lat ~ Lat:	$10°$	Nat. Hav.	$\underline{\cdot 00760}$	
			25744	
		=	$60° 58 \cdot 8 \ = $	$3,659 \ M$

<u>Rhumb line</u>   Meridional Parts.

Lat.	$38°$	$2453 \cdot 85$
Lat:	$48°$	$\underline{3274 \cdot 13}$
	D.M.P.	$820 \cdot 28$

D. Long: $87°$ =	$5,220'$ = log	$3 \cdot 71767$
D. M. P.	$820 \cdot 28$ = −log	$\underline{2 \cdot 91396}$
	log tan:	$0 \cdot 80371$

	= log sec:	$0 \cdot 80901$
D. Lat: $10°$ =	$600'$ = log	$\underline{2 \cdot 77815}$
	log	$3 \cdot 58716 \ = $ $3,865 \ M$.

<u>Rhumb line exceeds Great Circle by   206 M.</u>

* <u>A L T E R N A T I V E L Y , U S I N G N.P. 401, H.O. 229 on H.D 486.</u>

LHA	(= D. Lon.)	$87°$	}	Hc $\quad 29° 01'$
	(= Lat:)	$48°$	}	= CZD $60° 59'$
Dec:	(= Lat:)	$38°$	}	= $\quad \underline{3,659 \ MILES}$

17 The chronometer, whether 2-day or 8-day, should be wound up daily, preferably at about the same time each day (say at midday).

Answers 6

1   1975   Feb 15th   DR. 30° 20' S. 50° 30' E.

        Mer: Pass: 12.14 LMT.
        DR. Long: 50°30'E   − 3 22
                            0 8 52 GrMT at DR.

       Sextant Alt: L.L. , 72°02'.8. Brg: N.
                I E. − 1'.6
                Dip − 2.4   − 4.0
                        71° 58.8
             Corr: + 15.9
         TRUE ALT: 72° 14.7 N.
            from 90°
         T.Z.D.   17° 45.3 S
   Dec: 08^h 12°51'.0 S
  d − 0.9, 52^m − 0.8 12° 50.2 S
         LAT: 30° 35'.5 S

2

1975 Feb 15th afternoon. DR. 46°40'S. 167°20'E. I.E.-3'5, HE 10ft.

assume   16.00 LMT.

DR Long: 167°20'E — 11 09

04 51   after GMT.

Chron: 05-50-05

D.W.E. +   3 - 45

less   05 - 53 - 50   GMT.

GHA 05h   251° 26.8   Dec: S 12° 53.5.

53-50   13° 27.5   d,-0.9   −0.8.

264° 54.3   S 12° 52.7.

C.P. Long: E+ 167° 05.7

432°

− 360°

LHA   72°

C.P. Lat: S 47°

Dec: S 12° 53'

Hc   20° 59'

d + 43   + 38

TAB: ALT: 21° 37'

Sextant Alt: L.L   21° 18.3

IE   −3.5

Dip − 3.1   −6.6

21° 11.7

Corn: + 13.8

TRUE ALT: 21° 25.5

TAB: 21° 37.0

Intercept: AWAY 11.5

180°

Z   + 95

275° Zn

C.P.   47°S. 167°05.7 E.   Intercept: AWAY 11.5, bearing 275°

3

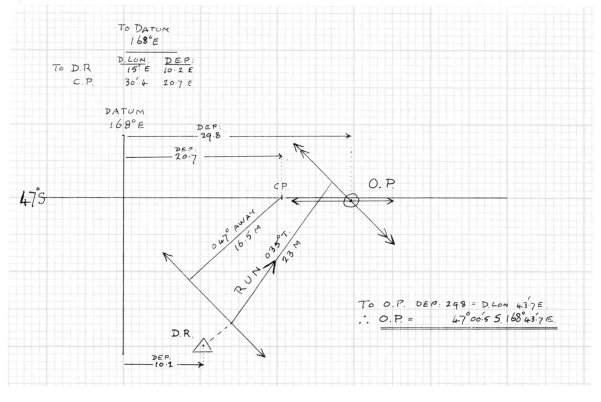

TO DATUM
168°E

	D. LON.	DEP.
TO D.R	15' E	10·2 E
C.P.	30'·4	20·7 E

DATUM
168°E

DEP.
29·8

DEP.
20·7

C.P.

O.P.

47°S

047° AWAY
16·5 M

RUN 035°T.
23 M

D.R.

DEP.
10·1

TO O.P. DEP. 29·8 = D.LON 43·7E.
∴ O.P. = 47°00'·5 S. 168°43'·7 E.

4

1975 Feb 16ᵗʰ   DR. 42°N. 65°W.

	C. Twilight	Sun RISE	Sun SET	C. Twilight	
In N 40°	06·25	06·53	17·36	18·04	L M T.
45°	06 30	07 01	17 28	17 59	"
Change of 5° =	+ 5	+ 8	− 8	− 5	
∴ " " 2° =	+ 2	+ 3	− 3	− 2	
∴ N 42° =	06 27	06 56	17 33	18 02	
Long: in time, 65°W	+ 4 20	+ 4 20	+ 4 20	+ 4 20	
	10 47	11 16	21 53	22 22	G.M.T.

157

5

Feb. 15th in DR. 40°S. 169°E

Dawn, about 15^D 0500 LMT.
DR. Long: 169°E — 1116
 G.D. 14^D 1744 approx GMT.

Chronometer: 6^h 28^m
 DWE. Fast — 6·45^s
  6 21 15.

∴ GD 14^D 18-21-15 GMT.
169°E is in Z-11,* + 11
 Local Date 15^D 05-21-15 Zone Time Z-11

Set ship's clock to 5^h 21^m

Head log book time column: Z - 11
enter   "   " date Feb 15th

* "Longitude East, Greenwich Time LEAST" (than Local time)
 "   "   West.   "   "   BEST " ("   "   ")

6

$$\frac{Z + 12}{Sept\ 10^{th}\ \ 23\ 45}$$

$$\frac{Z - 12}{Sept\ 12^{th}\ \ 00\ 15}$$

Ship's clock and Chronometer remain UNALTERED.

7

1975 Aug 29th p.m. twilight. DR. 38°20'N. 136°15'W.

C. Twilight, 29^D 1900 approx LMT.
DR. Long: 136°15'W + 905
 G.D. 30^D 0405 approx. GMT.

chron: 03-54-32 GMT.

GHA Aries 30ᴰ 03ʰ 22° 41.4
      54-32 13° 40.2
             36° 21.6
            +360
           396° 21.6
DR. Long: W − 136° 15.0
  LHA ♈ 260° 06.6

Sextant Alt: POLARIS 38° 07.4
    IE −5.0
    Dip −3.1   −8.1
           37° 59.3
    Corn: −1.2
           37° 58.1
  A_0 1° 33.1
  A_1 0.5
  A_2 0.9
        39° 32.6
        −1°
LAT: 38° 32.6

8

1975 Aug 31ˢᵗ a.m. twilight DR 42° 0'S. 163° 30'E.

check yr GD. C. Twilight 31ᴰ 0600 LMT.
  D.R. Long: 163° 30'E − 1054
      GD. 30ᴰ 1906 approx GMT.

    Chron: 18-53-49 GMT.

GHA Jupiter 30ᴰ 18ʰ 225° 15.0 Dec: N 7° 59.7
    53-49 13° 27.3 d, −0.1 −0.1
  v. 2.6   2.3 N 7° 59.6
      238° 44.6
CP. Long: E + 163° 15.4
    402°
    −360
  L.H.A. 42°
CP. Lat: S 42°
  Dec: N 8° 0'

Sextant Alt: JUPITER. 26° 43.8
  IE. −1.6
  Dip −2.4 −4.0
      26° 39.8
  Corn: −1.9
TRUE ALT: 26° 37.9
TAB: " 26° 59.0
Intercept: AWAY 21.1

TAB: ALT: Hc 26° 59

    180°
Z + 132°
    312° Zn.

9

1975   May 20^(th)   dawn twilight   DR. 42°S. 160°30'E.

<u>PRE-CALC:</u>   C. Twilight   20^D 0637 LMT
  DR. Long: 160°30'E —   1042
        G.D. 19^D 1955 GMT.

GHA Aries 19^D 19^h   161° 49'5
        55^m   13° 47.3.
             175° 36.8

  C P Long: E + 160° 23.2.
      LHA ♈   336°
  CP Lat: S 42°

        Approx:
        Alt. Bearing.
  ⎰ Diphda   52° 09'   062°
  ⎨ Miaplacidus 22° 23'   173°
  ⎩ ALTAIR.   28° 08   316°

<u>SIGHTS TAKEN</u>	DIPHDA	MIAPLACIDUS	ALTAIR.
at G.M.T.	19-52-13	19-52-46	19-53-12.

GHA ♈ 19^D 19^h   161° 49'5   161° 49'5   161° 49'5
    52-13.   13° 05.4   52-46 13° 13.7   53-12 13° 20.2.
         174° 54.9   175° 03.2   175° 09.7.
  C.P. Long: E+ 160 05.1   160° 56.8   160° 50.3.
      LHA ♈   335°   336°   336°
  C.P. Lat: S 42°   S 42°   S 42°

        Hc   51° 30'   22° 23'   28° 08'
        Zn   063°   173°   316°

<u>Sextant Alt: ✶</u>   51° 47'9   22° 19.7   28° 28'2
  IE + 1.3
  Dip — 2.7   — 1.4   — 1.4   — 1.4
         51° 46.5   22° 18.3   28° 26.8
    Corn: — 0.8   — 2.4   — 1.8
  TRUE ALT: 51° 45.7   22° 15.9   28° 25.0
   TAB: "   51° 30.0   22° 23.0   28° 08.0.
<u>Intercept:</u>   TO 15.7   AWAY 7.1   TO 17.0

<u>O.P. 41° 56' S. 160° 24' E</u>

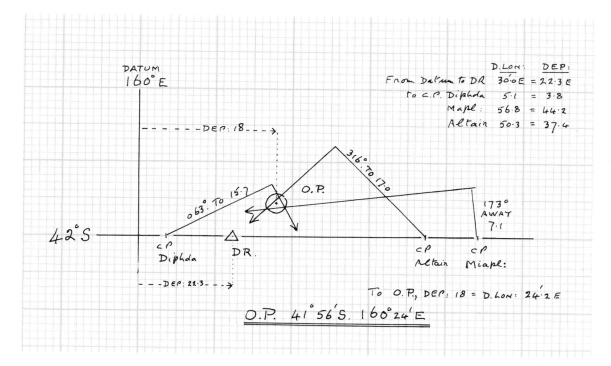

DATUM
160°E

	D.LON:	DEP:
From Datum to DR	30·0 E =	22·3 E
to C.P. Diphda	5·1 =	3·8
Maple:	56·8 =	44·2
Altain	50·3 =	37·4

- - - - - - -DEP: 18- - - →

063°. To 15·7

O.P.

316°. To 17·0

173°
AWAY
7·1

42°S

cP
Diphda

DR.

cP
Altain

cP
Miapl:

- - -DEP: 22·3- - - →

To O.P., DEP: 18 = D.LON: 24·2 E

O.P. 41° 56' S. 160° 24' E

Answers 6

10

1975 Aug 29th DR. 34°10'S. 152°E.   I.E. −4'2, HE 8ft.

check yo GD.   p.m. twilight 29^D 1806 LMT
DR. Long: 152°E −   1008
GD 29^D 0758 GMT.

		SPICA		ARCTURUS.	
		at GMT 29^D 07-53-54.		07-54-32.	
SHA ✳		159°01·4	S 11°02·1	146°21·7	N19°18·7
GHA ♈	07^h	81° 52·1		81° 52·1	
	53-54	13° 30·7		54-32. 13° 40·2.	
GHA ✳		254° 24·2		241° 54·0	
CP. Long:		E+ 152° 35·8		152° 06·0	
		407°		394°	
		− 360		−360	
L.H.A. ✳		47°		34°	
CP. Lat:		S 34°		S 34°	
Dec:		S 11°02'		N 19°19'	

	Hc	41°26'		Hc	27°54'
d, +35		+ 1	d, −52		−16.
TAB:ALT:		41° 27'	TAB:ALT:		27°38'

Z + 180°
     107°
     287° Zm

Z + 180°
     143°
     323° Zm.

Sextant Alt: 41° 52'·9
IE −4'·2
Dip −2·7   −6·9
41° 46·0
Corn: −1·1
TRUE ALT: 41° 44·9
TAB: " 41° 27·0
Intercept: To 17·9

27° 34'·8

−6·9
27° 27·9
−1·9
27° 26·0
27° 38·0.
AWAY 12·0.

162

11

1975   Aug. 30ᵗʰ   a.m. C Twilight   DR 42°40'S. 162°15'E.   IE −1.4, HE 6 ft.

Check yr. GD.   CT   30ᴰ 0602   LMT
DR Long: 162°15'E   −   10 49
G.D.   29ᴰ   1913   CₜMT.

Read chron: as 29ᴰ 18-55-12 GMT.

GHA MOON 29ᴰ 18ʰ   186°01'5   Dec: N 20°06'8   H.P. 56'0.
            55-12   13°10.8   d,+3.3   + 3.1
v. 10.0   9.3   N 20° 09'9
                  199° 21.6
C.P. Long: E + 162° 38.4
            362°

        LHA   002°   Sextant Alt: MOON U.L. 26°34'6
C.P. Lat: S 43°   IE −1.4
Dec: N 20° 10'   Dip −2.4   −3.8
                                            26°30.8
    Hc   26° 58'   Corn: 60.3
d, −60   −10.   H.P. 56'0   2.5.
TAB: ALT: 26° 48'   27°33.6.
                              for U.L.   − 30.0
        180°   TRUE ALT: 27° 03.6
Z   + 178   TAB: "   26° 48.0
    358° Zn   Intercept: To 15.6

C.P.   43°S. 162°38.4 E   Intercept. To 15.6 Bearing 358°

12

1975 Feb 17th MOON MER: PASS. DR 40°S. 158°E

Mer: Pass: 17^D 1637 GMT at 0°. | 16^D 1551
Corr: for Long 158°E − 20 (a) | 17^D 1637
_____ | 1 day. 360°. 46^m (a)
17^D 1617 | 158°E = $\frac{158}{360}$ × 46^m = 20^m
D.R. Long 158°E − 1032 |
G.D. 17^D 0545 GMT at DR. ☒

Sextant Alt: MOON L.L. 33° 31ʹ0 N.
IE − 2ʹ5
Dip − 2·4
− 4·9
33° 26·1
Corr: 57·3
H.P. 55·3 2·3
TRUE ALT: 34° 25·7 N
from 90°
T.Z.D. 55° 34·3 S
Dec: 05^h 15° 14ʹ1 N
d. + 8·4, 45^m + 6·3 15° 20·4 N

L A T: 40° 13·9 S.

☒ Alternative Method, to nearest second.

Required LHA 0° or 360°
D.R. Long: E − 158°
∴ req^d GHA is 202°

191° 14ʹ7 = 05^h
remainder 10° 45·3
v. 12·8, 44^m 9·5
10° 35·8 = 44^m 24^s

MER: PASS: TIME: 05-44-24 GMT at DR.

PROOF.
GHA 05^h 191° 14·7
44-24 10° 35·7
v. 12·8 9·5
201° 59·9
DR Long: E+ 158°
359° 59·9
·1
= 0°
∴ on the meridian 158°E

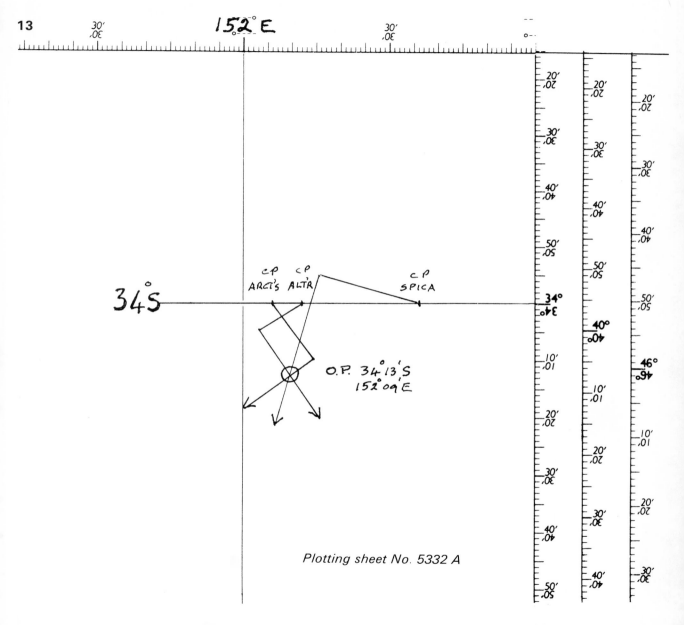

13

152° E

34° S

CP ARCT'S CP ALT'R

CP SPICA

O.P. 34° 13' S
152° 09' E

Plotting sheet No. 5332 A

14

1975   Feb 16ᵗ.   Compass Check.   DR. 39° 20' S   143° 30' E.

Check for G.D.   16ᴰ 0900   assumed LMT.
DR. Long: 143° 30' E —   9 34.
                    G.D 15ᴰ 23 26   assumed G.MT.

Use 15ᴰ 21-54-13 G.M.T.

G.HA 15ᴰ 21ʰ   131° 27'.3   Dec: S 12° 39'.8
      54-13.   13° 33.3   d-0.9   −0.8
                   145° 00.6   S 12° 39'.0
C.P. Long: E + 143° 59.4
     L.H.A   289°
C.P Lat: S 39°
    Dec: S 12° 39'
              180°
    Z − 92
           088° Zn.

S̲u̲n̲'s̲ ̲b̲e̲a̲r̲i̲n̲g̲ ̲b̲y̲ ̲c̲o̲m̲p̲a̲s̲s̲   085° c
              Variation   + 12° E
                              097° M.
              Sun's Azimuth   088° T
          ∴ D̲E̲V̲I̲A̲T̲I̲O̲N̲   9° W

(on yacht's heading at the time.)

Variation   12° E
Deviation   9° W
T̲OTAL ERROR   3° E.

15.a

1975 Feb 15ᵗʰ MER: PASS: DR 48°S. 105°W. I.E. −2.3, H.E. 8 ft.

Mer: Pass. 15ᴰ 12 14 L.M.T.
DR Long: 105°W + 7 00
————————————
19 14 GMT. at DR.

Sextant Alt: L.L. 54° 21.3 bng: N.
I.E −2.3
Dip −2.7   −5.0
—————————
54° 16.3
Corr: + 15.5
TRUE ALT: 54° 31.8 N
from 90°
—————————
T.Z.D.   35° 28.2   S

Dec: 19ʰ 12° 41.5 S
d, −0.9. 14ᵐ   −0.2   12° 41.3 S
———————————————
LAT: 48° 09.5 S

Log 474.0 M
497.0
—————
RUN 23 M.   Co. 140° T.   Per plot, new DR 48° 25'S. 104° 38'W.

Check yor G.D. assume 15ᴰ 1600 LMT
Long: 104° 30'W + 6 58
——————————
G.D 15ᴰ 22 58 GMT. ∴ Read chron: as 22-54-02 GMT.

G.HA 22ʰ 146° 27.3   Dec: S 12° 39.0
54-02   13° 30.5   d, −0.9   − 0.8
——————————   —————————
159° 57.8   S 12° 38.2
C.P. Long: W − 104° 57.8
L.H.A.   55°
C.P. Lat: S 48°   Sextant Alt: L.L.   31° 48.0
Dec: S 12° 38'   I.E. & Dip   −5.0
——————————
31° 43.0
Hc   32° 00'   Corn: + 14.7
d, +46   + 29   TRUE ALT: 31° 57.7
—————————   TAB: "   32° 29.0
TAB: ALT: 32° 29'   —————————————
180°   Intercept: AWAY 31.3
Z   + 109
—————————
289° Zn   O.P. 48° 27'S. 104° 23'W.

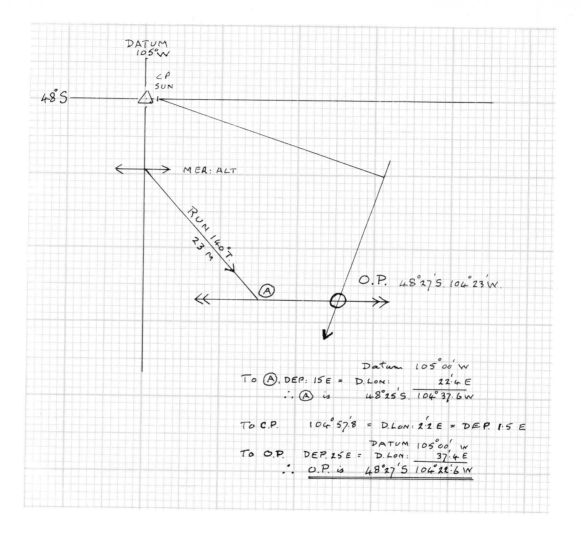

To (A). DEP. 15 E = D.LON: 22′·4 E

∴ (A) is 48°25′S. 104°37·6 W

To C.P. 104°57′·8 = D.LON: 2·2′ E = DEP. 1·5 E

To O.P. DEP. 25 E = D.LON: 37′·4 E

∴ O.P. is 48°27′S 104°22·6 W

b

O.P. Feb 15th 1600 LMT.   48°27'S   104°23'W

RUN : Co 135°T = S 45°E. 132 M. = D.Lat: 93·3 = 1°33·3 S
                          DEP: 93·3 E
Current 140° = S 40°E 13 M = D.Lat: 10·0 S
                    DEP: 8·4 E
                          101·7 E
              in M.Lat: 49° = D.Lon: 155' =   2°35'E.
    D.R. Feb 16th p.m. 1800.   50°10·3 S 101°48'W.

Check for G.D.   16^D 19·00 assumed LMT.
    Long: 102°W +   6·48
              G.D. 17^D 01·48   ~   GMT.

	MOON	SUN
Sights taken at	17^D 00-52-27	00-53-12 GMT.

GHA. 17^D 00^h   118°35·0 Dec N 14°31·2. H.P.55·2.   176°28·2. Dec. S 12°16·5
         52-27   12°30·9 d+8·7 +7·6   53-12. 13°18·0. d-0·9 —0·8
    V: 13·1   11·5   N 14°38·8   S 12°15·7
                 131°17·4   189°46·2.
C.P. Long: W — 101°17·4   — 101°46·2.
     L.H.A.   30°   88°
C.P. Lat: S 50°   S 50°
     Dec: N 14°39'   S 12°16'

      Hc 20°47'   180°   Hc 10°26'   180°
    d — 56   —36   Z + 149   d + 46   + 12   Z + 84
    TAB: ALT: 20°11'   329° Zn.   TAB: ALT: 10°38'   264° Zn

Sextant Alt: MOON U.L. 19°52·9   SUN. L.L. 10°46·7
          I.E — 2·3
          Dip — 2·7   — 5·0   — 5·0.
                      19°47·9   10°41·7
          Conn: 62·2.   Conn: + 11·3.
     H.P. 55·2   1·9.
                      20°52·0.
          for U.L.   —30·0.
    TRUE ALT: 20°22·0.   TRUE ALT 10°53·0.
    TAB: "   20°11·0.   TAB: "   10°38·0.
Intercept: TO 11·0.   TO   15·0.

        O.P. 50°07'S. 102°08'W.

169

Answers 6

Plotting sheet No. 5331 A

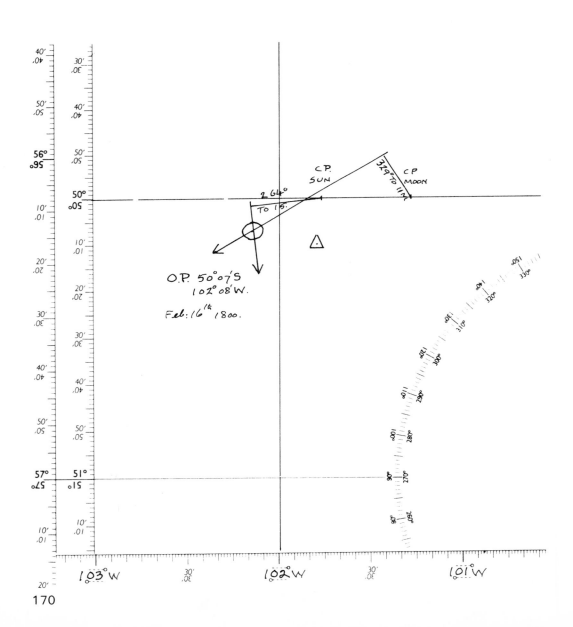

O.P. 50°07'S
102°08'W.

Feb: 16ᵗʰ 1800.

c.

Feb. GD 17^D DR. 50°15'S. 101°24'W.   IE −2.3. Ht.E 8ft.

	Souhail	Achernar	Aldebaran	SATURN.
Time. GMT.	02-53-04	02-53-46	02-54-17	02-54-50.

GHA ♈   176°26.0   176°26.0   176°26.0   Saturn 72°51.1   Dec: N22°32.8
            13°18.2   13°28.7   13°36.5   13°42.5   d.00.
                                                         v. 2.6   2.4
            ─────   ─────   ─────   86°36.0.
            189°44.2.   189°54.7   190°02.5   + 360
                                                                  446°36.0.
C.P. Long: W−101°44.2.   101°54.7   101°02.5   101°36.0.
   L.H.A.♈ 88°   88°   89°   Saturn. 345°
C.P. Lat: S 50°   S 50°   S 50°   S 50°
                                                         Dec: N 22°33'

Hc 56°30'   52°57'   21°09'   Hc 16°47'
                                                     d−59   −32
Zn 098°   233°   339°   TAB: ALT: 16°15'
                                                     −   180°
                                                           Z   −166
                                                               014° Zn.

Sextant Alt:	56°31.4	53°15.0	21°09.6	16°00.4
IE −2.3				
Dip −2.7	−5.0	−5.0	−5.0	−5.0.
	56°26.4	53°10.0	21°04.6	15°55.4.
Corr:	−0.6	−0.7	−2.6	−3.4.
TRUE ALT:	56°25.8	53°09.3	21°02.0	15°52.0.
TAB: "	56°30.0	52°57.0	21°09.0	16°15.0.
Intercept:	AWAY 4.2	TO 12.3	AWAY 7.0	AWAY 23.0.

O.P. 50°21'S. 101°55'W.

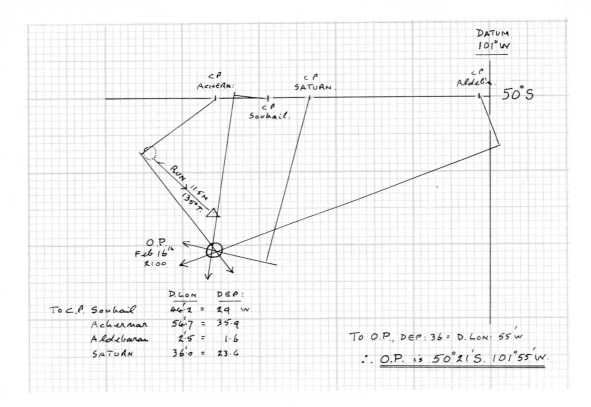

DATUM
101° W

cP
ACHERN:

cP
SATURN.

cP
Aldeb'n

50° S

cP
Souhail.

RUN 11.5 M
135° T.

O.P.
Feb 16th
2100

	D. LON	DEP:
To C.P. Souhail	44.2 =	29 W
Achernar	54.7 =	35.9
Aldebaran	2.5 =	1.6
SATURN	36.0 =	23.6

To O.P., DEP: 36 = D. LON: 55 W

∴ O.P. is 50° 21' S. 101° 55' W.

16

Composite Gt. Circle track between 30°S. 32°E & 48°S. 165°E
not further S than 55°S.

Gt. Circle Diagram N°5029 -   Long: 32°E
                                   165°E
                        D. Long: 133°   Use Mid Long: 100°E.

Composite Track taken from
Diagram every 10° Long.

		Haversine / Cosine Formula	OR	Using N.P. 401, H.O.229 or H.D.486.

INTERMEDIATE POINTS

1st G.C. 30° S. 32°E.   D. Long: 68° logHav: 9.49512   L.H.A. 68°
        37°   40°   Lat: 30° logCos 9.93753   Lat: 55°
        43°30'   50°   Lat: 55° logCos 9.75859   Dec: 30°
        48°   60°   logHav 9.19124
        51°30'   70°   = Nat. Hav. .15533.
        53°30'   80°   Lat ~ Lat 25° "   " .04685.
        54°50'   90°   .20218   Hc 36°34
        55°   100°   CZD = 53°26'   from 90°
                                                             C.Z.D. 53°26
                            MILES = 3,206   = 3,206 M

Parallel Sailing along 55°S (See below)

2nd G.C. 55° S. 130°E.   D. Long 35° logHav: 8.95628   L.H.A 35°
        54°   140°   Lat: 55° logCos 9.75859   Lat: 55°
        52°30'   150°   Lat: 48° logCos 9.82551   Dec: 48°
        50°   160°   logHav 8.54038
        48°   165°   Nat. .03471   Hc 67°23'
                            Lat ~ Lat 7° "   .00373.   from 90°
                                          .03844
                                  CZD = 22°37'   22°37'
                            MILES = 1.357.   1,357. M.

Parallel Sailing. D. Long: 30° = 1,800 D. Lon
                    in Lat 55° = DEP: 1,032. Miles

        SUMMARY.
1st Gt. Circle track   3,206
Parallel Sailing   1,032
2nd Gt. Circle track.   1,357
                            5,595   MILES.

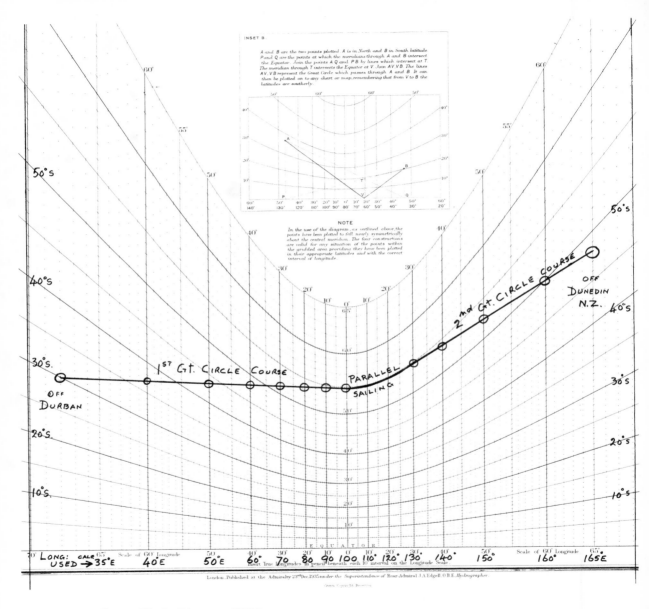

Great Circle Diagram 5029

April 10th error 4^m 06^s Slow
,,   18th   ,,   3   46 Slow
          in   8 days,   20^s Gain, = 2^s·5 per day.
May 4th. Error on Apr. 18th 3^m 46^s Slow

          Apr.   18–30, 12 days
          May   1–4.   4
16 × 2·5 = −40^s Gain
          Accumulated error 3^m 06^s Slow.
                    Chronometer 04^h 18^m 13^s
          Accumulated error   + 3   06 Slow
                    04^h 21^m 19^s GMT.

TABLES

To answer the questions the following tables are required:

Nautical Almanac 1975 (issued by Nautical Almanac Office, Royal Greenwich Observatory and Nautical Almanac Office, U.S. Naval Observatory).

Sight Reduction Tables for Air Navigation (AP 3270 or HO 249, U.S.) Volumes 1 and 3.

Some answers have been shown as an alternative, using NP 401 or HO 229, U.S.

Chapters 1, 2 and 3 can be answered using the extracts from Sight Reduction tables given in Ocean Yacht Navigator by Kenneth Wilkes. For the remaining chapters, the actual tables are needed. Relevant extracts from the Nautical Almanac 1975 are also given in Ocean Yacht Navigator.